All-Ireland History Quiz Book

Jim Doherty and Denis Hickey

GILL AND MACMILLAN

To my many friends
in Telecom Eireann,
Estuary House, Limerick:
for being there

Denis Hickey

Published in Ireland by
Gill and Macmillan Ltd
Goldenbridge
Dublin 8
with associated companies in
Auckland, Delhi, Gaborone, Hamburg, Harare,
Hong Kong, Johannesburg, Kuala Lumpur, Lagos, London,
Manzini, Melbourne, Mexico City, Nairobi,
New York, Singapore, Tokyo
© J. E. Doherty and D. J. Hickey, 1989
0 7171 1707 3
Print origination by Irish Typesetting and Publishing Co. Ltd, Galway
Printed by Richard Clay, Suffolk

Questions

1. Who was responsible in A.D. 120 for the first map of Ireland?

2. Name the first yacht to carry the Irish flag around the world.

3. What was the first monastery to be built in the Gothic style, heralding the end of native building traditions?

4. Who was the first Irish representative to the European Court of Justice?

5. Where was Proportional Representation first used in an Irish election?

6. What was Ireland's first regular Sunday newspaper?

7. Who was the first Northern Ireland resident to become a member of Seanad Eireann?

8. Who was the first lawyer to present a case to the European Commission of Human Rights?

9. James Bond was the inventive station-master of which station, the first in Ireland to be lit by electricity — from a windmill erected by him?

10. Which was the first Irish city to obtain a charter?

11. What made its first appearance in Howth and Drogheda during August 1348?

12. What 'first' was accomplished by Richard Crosbie on 19 January 1785?

13. The first Feis Tara was held one thousand years before the birth of Christ. Which law-making king instigated the Assembly?

14. During the reign of which Ard-Ri (High King) did the first Viking invasion occur?

Answers on page 71

1. Who was the Northern Ireland representative on the Boundary Commission, 1924–5?

2. What opened to the public in Northern Ireland on 2 July 1964?

3. What organisation met for the first time in the Ulster Minor Hall, Belfast on 3 March 1905?

4. Who founded the Union Defence League in 1907?

5. What was the aim of the Local Option Party in Northern Ireland?

6. Of which bishop did Lord Charlemont say that he was 'a bad father, a worse husband . . . greatly addicted to intrigue and roguery'?

7. What significant Unionist organisation was established on 1 May 1885?

8. Who became Northern Ireland GOC on 4 February 1971?

9. What was Gerry Fitt's occupation before he entered full-time politics?

10. Who succeeded Lord Craigavon as PM of Northern Ireland in 1940?

11. Which Ulsterman led a pressure group of British MPs seeking civil rights in Northern Ireland in the 1950s?

12. Who led the official Nationalist opposition at Stormont from 1965 to 1969?

13. Who led the Unionist Party from 1906 to 1910?

14. Who became Secretary for Northern Ireland in May 1979?

15. What organisation was founded by Billy Hull in 1971?

Answers on page 71

1. To whom did Cecil Rhodes offer the advice 'Resign — marry — return', by telegram, in December 1890?

2. Who, speaking on the Coinage Bill in the Senate on 3 May 1926, said, '... designs in connection with postage stamps and coinage may be described ... as the silent ambassadors on national taste'?

3. Who said, during August 1969, 'The Catholics have been interfering in Ulster affairs since 1641'?

4. Of whom did Henry VII say, 'Then he is fit to rule all Ireland seeing that all Ireland cannot rule him'?

5. Who, speaking in Dail Eireann on 17 December 1921, said, 'The only pleasure in freedom is fighting for it'?

6. Parnell, speaking in Cork on 21 January 1885, said, 'We cannot under the British Constitution ask for more than the restitution of Grattan's Parliament ...'. Complete the sentence.

7. Who, speaking in support of the Act of Union, said, 'I would have the two sisters [England and Ireland] embrace like one brother'?

8. Which politician commented on 16 July 1971, 'The courts are open to anyone — like the Ritz!'?

9. Who, speaking on the Intoxicating Liquor Bill in Dail Eireann on 23 March 1927, said, 'When I think of the hardship involved in having only seven hours to drink on Sunday, my soul shudders!'?

10. Which English historian observed that the Cromwellian settlement had made the Irish '... hewers of wood and drawers of water'?

Answers on page 72

1. Who was the last leader of the Irish Parliamentary Party?

2. Who was Minister for Local Government from December 1957 to November 1966?

3. Who became leader of the Labour Party in 1960?

4. Which Senator was Minister for Agriculture from March to November 1957?

5. Which Irishman was 'Father of the House of Commons' and official British Film Censor from 1917?

6. Who was Minister for Education from 1932 to 1948?

7. Who was Minister for Justice from 1939 to 1948?

8. Who founded the All-for-Ireland League in 1910?

9. Who was Ceann Comhairle of the first Dail Eireann (21 January 1919)?

10. What party did William Magennis found as a breakaway from Cumann na nGaedheal (1925)?

11. Upon whose death did Parnell win the Meath seat in 1875?

12. What party was founded by Michael Donnellan in 1938?

13. What political party won two out of three by-elections held in 1947?

14. Which President of Ireland once worked as advertising manager of the *Irish Press*?

15. In what year was the election sometimes known as the 'Pact Election'?

Answers on page 72

1. What organisation was founded by Bulmer Hobson in 1905?

2. Who founded the Irish Transvaal Society to organise support for the Boers?

3. Who founded the Templecrone Co-Operative Society in 1906 with capital of £1.75p?

4. Who founded and edited *The Tablet*, first in London (1840) and in Dublin from 1850?

5. What organisation numbered P. J. Ryan and John McKay among its founders?

6. What Abbey was founded in 1126 by Cathal Craobh-dearg O'Connor?

7. Who founded the Wolfe Tone Society in 1963?

8. What did Rev. James Graves establish in 1849 in Kilkenny?

9. Where did Mr Jeffreys build a noted linen and wool-preserving centre in the eighteenth century?

10. What did Fr Farrell found in 1927?

11. Who founded the Catholic Young Men's Society?

12. What did Patricia and Con McCluskey of Dungannon found in 1967?

13. What movement did William O'Brien found in 1898?

14. Where did Sir William Cox, Lord Chancellor of England, build a town to house his plantation of weavers?

15. Who built the town of Bandon, Co. Cork?

Answers on page 73

1. Who gave the name 'Fenians' to the movement?

2. Name the author of *The Felon's Track* (1867).

3. Who organised the rescue of Kelly and Deasy at Manchester on 18 September 1867?

4. Which French general was placed in command of the Fenians' 1867 rising?

5. Who succeeded James Stephens as Head Centre of the IRB, 1866–7?

6. Name the author of the ballad 'God Save Ireland' in honour of Allen, Larkin and O'Brien.

7. Who arrested Godfrey Massey at Limerick Junction in March 1867?

8. Which clerical apologist for the Fenians delivered a lecture on 'The Catholic Doctrine of the Right of Revolution' in February 1867?

9. Who captured Ballyhurst Fort, Co. Tipperary on 6 March 1867?

10. Who betrayed the Fenian plans for the raid on Chester Castle, 1867?

11. Name the priest who officiated at the graveside of Terence Bellew McManus in 1861.

12. For what were Joseph Brady, Daniel Curley, Timothy Kelly, Michael Fagan and Thomas Caffrey executed?

13. Who founded the Phoenix Societies in the 1850s?

14. Which Fenian leader served in the French Foreign Legion?

15. For whom was 'Hell . . . not hot enough nor eternity long enough to punish' the Fenians?

Answers on page 73

1. Who in 1273 became Cork's first Mayor?

2. Name the oldest Catholic church in Cork.

3. In what year were an English governor and garrison installed for the first time in Cork City?

4. Why was Maurice Roche, Mayor of Cork, presented with a silver collar by Queen Elizabeth I (1571)?

5. In what year were the bells of Shandon first installed?

6. Who was Guest of Honour when five Mayors attended dinner at the Lancastrian Schools in Cork on 8 April 1844?

7. What event brought a huge crowd to Cork on 17 May 1869?

8. Who in 1900 became the city's first Lord Mayor?

9. Who designed Queen's College, later University College, Cork?

10. In what year did Cork have three Lord Mayors?

11. When were automatic traffic lights first installed in Cork City?

12. What occurred in Cork City on 12 December 1955?

13. When was Cork Airport opened to traffic?

14. In what year did Cork celebrate its '800'?

15. In what year was the Cork Exhibition held?

Answers on page 74

1. Name the German spy who landed in Ireland in 1940, was interned and later committed suicide (23 May 1947).

2. Whose publication of *The North Began* led to the founding of the Irish Volunteers?

3. What famous ship went down off the Saltees on 8 May 1947?

4. Who was the first Republican TD to take the Oath of Allegiance in 1927?

5. Which Irish physicist shared the Nobel Prize for Physics?

6. Who was Minister for Defence in the first Fianna Fail government (1932)?

7. Which Home Rule MP for Cavan initiated the parliamentary tactic of 'obstructionism' in the 1870s?

8. Name the Chicago police chief and musicologist whose works include *Music of Ireland* (1903) and *Irish Folk Music* (1910).

9. Who died on hunger-strike on 25 September 1917?

10. Sean O'Casey was for a time Secretary of which organisation?

11. Who was Secretary to the Irish Delegation during the Anglo-Irish Treaty negotiations of 1921?

12. Who succeeded William Whitelaw as Northern Ireland Secretary?

13. Which Limerick journalist published a *Dictionary of Dates* (1841)?

14. John Charles McQuaid, Archbishop of Dublin 1940–72, was a native of which county?

Answers on page 75

1. Which name means 'horse-lord'?

2. Which name literally means 'son of the devotee of Jesus'?

3. Markree Castle, Co. Sligo was the ancestral home of which family?

4. Of which ancient family was Gort, Co. Galway the seat until the sixteenth century?

5. Curragh Chase, Co. Limerick, was the ancestral home of which literary family?

6. Which family owned Dunmanus Castle, Co. Cork?

7. What is a toponym?

8. In which province is the name Barry most widespread?

9. With which county since the seventeenth century is the name Bennis principally associated?

10. What is the name of one of ancient Munster's leading clans, whose name means 'loving'?

11. The name Cunningham was brought to Ireland by settlers from which country?

12. The name Davin is particularly associated with which county?

13. Which family crest features a chained cat?

14. Which family crest features a robin holding a laurel leaf in its beak?

15. 'All power from God' is the motto of which ancient Irish family whose coat of arms displays an oak tree uprooted?

Answers on page 75

1. Name the landlord whose evictions in Tipperary town led to the foundation of 'New Tipperary' in 1890.

2. For what evictions was Col John O'Callaghan responsible in June 1887?

3. What peasant movement was founded at Markethill, Co. Armagh in 1785?

4. Where in Co. Kilkenny did the confrontation, generally taken to be the start of the 'Tithe War', take place?

5. Who was the first priest arrested during the Land League agitation period?

6. Which Co. Galway landlord was murdered on 25 September 1880?

7. Who wrote the 'Plan of Campaign' in *United Ireland* in 1886?

8. Which pioneering land agitator died on 27 December 1849?

9. Where did the so-called 'Siege of Saunders' Fort' occur in August 1886?

10. Who was the Catholic priest who played a major role in the so-called 'War in Partry', Co. Mayo (1860)?

11. Name the priest who led the Land League in the area around Gweedore, Co. Donegal.

12. Which newspaper editor co-founded the Land League of Mayo with Davitt in 1879?

13. Where precisely were evictions carried out by John George Adair?

14. Which clergyman was known as 'The General' for his role in the Land War in the 1880s?

Answers on page 76

1. What was the newspaper of the Belfast United Irishmen?

2. Whose order for handing-in arms was the prelude to a reign of terror in Ulster?

3. Who, on trial for high treason, killed himself in the dock on 30 April 1795?

4. Who was both Lord Lieutenant and C-in-C during the 1798 Insurrection?

5. On what island did Napper Tandy land briefly in 1798?

6. Who said that the army in Ireland was 'in a state of licentiousness which must render it formidable to everyone but the enemy'?

7. Who succeeded Abercrombie as C-in-C in April 1798?

8. Which bishop of Killala wrote an eye-witness account of the French invasion of 1798?

9. Who carried a green flag for the United insurgents at Ballinahinch where she was killed?

10. Which Co. Wexford landlord was released from prison to become leader of the United Army for a brief period in 1798?

11. Who was for a short time President of the Republic of Connaught?

12. Which medical doctor and historian of the United Irishmen died on 5 February 1886?

13. Whose information to the government destroyed the chance of a successful rebellion in 1798?

14. Who, while betraying the United Irishmen in the 1790s, was being retained at the same time to defend them?

Answers on page 76

1. Who published the proselytising *Achill Missionary Herald and Western Witness* from 1837?

2. Name the Vatican representative who investigated 'boycotting' in Ireland in 1887.

3. Where did the eighteenth century Carmelite Fr Denis Mahony live as a recluse on an Irish monastic site?

4. What church was founded by William Walker?

5. Who was the first President of Maynooth College?

6. Which President of University College Cork became a priest following his retirement?

7. Archbishop McQuaid of Dublin condemned an international football match in 1955. Who were Ireland's opponents?

8. Where in Ireland was the only house of the Trinitarian Canons of the Order of the Redemption of Captives?

9. Which Irishman founded the Presbyterian Church in America?

10. Who received the 'regium donum' from 1672 until 1871?

11. What religious order sponsored the journal *Studies*?

12. Which Franciscan Bishop of Down and Connor was hanged for treason in 1612?

13. Whose first Irish foundation was established at Leighlinbridge c. 1270?

14. Which Pope is associated with the conversion of the Irish to Christianity?

15. Which Archbishop of Cashel was tortured by having his feet roasted in metal boots filled with boiling oil?

Answers on page 77

1. Who sailed the *Ranger* into Belfast Lough on 13 April 1778?

2. What ferry capsized off Co. Down on 31 January 1953, with the loss of one hundred and twenty eight lives?

3. Name any other yacht besides the *Asgard* involved in gun-running for the Irish Volunteers in 1914.

4. By what name was the Irish Naval Service first known?

5. What was the first ship built by William Ritchie at Belfast?

6. What ship rescued Fenians from Fremantle, Australia in 1876?

7. Who became known as the 'Father of Belfast ship-building'?

8. What luxury liner, containing over £5,000,000 worth of gold, sank off Fanad Head, Co. Donegal, on 3 January 1917?

9. What famous ship was commanded by Richard Roberts?

10. What ship made the first steam crossing from the Clyde to Belfast?

11. What ship at various stages had the names the *Castro* and the *Libau*?

12. Who was among the passengers on board the *Scourge* on 1 June 1848?

13. What ship caused severe pollution to West Cork in November 1986?

14. What were the *Hare* and the *Fraternity*?

15. What ship, intercepted off Waterford on 28 March 1973, was found to be running guns?

Answers on page 77

1. Who first held the title Earl of Pembroke in Ireland?

2. Whose nickname was 'Copper-faced Jack'?

3. By what name did James Fitzthomas Fitzgerald become famous?

4. By what other name was Reginald Ingram Montgomery Hitchcock better known?

5. Who was sometimes known as the 'Fighting Priest of Gweedore'?

6. What is the name of the so-called 'Sixth of George the First'?

7. By what name was the *Helga* known when it served as a fishery protection vessel in the 1920s?

8. Who was known as the 'King of the Irish Pipers'?

9. By what name is Michael Moran better known?

10. What was the stage-name of Peter C. Judge?

11. For which of James Joyce's characters is Oliver St John Gogarty the supposed model?

12. Who sometimes used the pseudonym 'The Man in the Cloak' for his publications in the *Nation*?

13. What was the pen-name of James Sullivan Starkey?

14. Which Cork soldier earned the title 'Liberator of Greece'?

15. What was the real name of the 'Tailor' in *The Tailor and Ansty*?

Answers on page 78

1. What did John Feely found in 1950?

2. What did Burton Conyngham found in 1782?

3. Who, along with Henry Harrison, founded the Irish Dominion League in 1919?

4. Name the studio founded by Sarah Purser in 1903.

5. Who founded Christus Rex?

6. Who founded the Loft in Cork?

7. Who founded the Irish Women Workers' Union?

8. What nineteenth-century organisation was founded by Joshua Jacob?

9. Name either of the two priests who founded the *Irish Monthly*.

10. What organisation did Thomas Langlois Lefroy establish in 1828 to preserve 'the integrity of the Protestant religion'?

11. What organisation was founded by Rev. Dr Denis Fahy in the 1940s?

12. What did the Earl of Rosse, Jack St Leger and James Worsdale found in 1735?

13. Who founded the Central Catholic Library in 1962?

14. Who founded St Ita's School, modelled on Pearse's St Enda's?

15. What did Joseph Robinson found in 1834?

Answers on page 78

1. Name the Commission appointed by Gladstone to investigate the workings of the 1870 Land Act and to examine agricultural conditions.

2. Where is the oldest surviving Church of Ireland church?

3. Name the paper founded by Noel Doherty and Ian Paisley on 13 February 1966.

4. Who became President of Munster on 6 March 1600?

5. Who led the officers in the so-called Curragh 'Mutiny' of March 1914?

6. Who arranged the music for 'Moore's Melodies'?

7. Name the Commission which in August 1969 inquired into the recruitment and organisation of the RUC.

8. Which Italian became Mayor of Clonmel in 1844?

9. What linked the Irish Shipping vessels, *Irish Pine* and *Irish Oak*?

10. Who was the longest-serving Lord Lieutenant of Ireland?

11. In which field did Arthur Jacob (1790–1874) achieve fame?

12. What Irish secondary school was established 'to furnish the gentry . . . with a school on the model of Eton'?

13. Who was Governor of the Central Bank during 1953–60?

14. Which unpopular landlord was murdered near Mulroy Bay, Co. Donegal, in 1878?

15. What appeared for the first time on the streets of Belfast on 28 August 1872?

Answers on page 79

1. What was the official IRB newspaper from 1863 to 1865?

2. Who edited the comic newspaper *The Jarvey*?

3. Who founded the *Protestant Guardian* in the nineteenth century?

4. What newspaper was founded by the Irish Agricultural Organisation Society (IAOS)?

5. Who edited the *Irish Times* from 1934 to 1954?

6. What paper had for its sub-title 'American Industrial Liberator'?

7. Who was the first editor of the *Irish Press* (1931)?

8. Who was the editor of the *Irish People*, 1863–5?

9. Who was editing Parnell's *United Ireland* at the time of the split (1890)?

10. Who was the first 'Quidnunc' of the *Irish Times*?

11. Who was the founder of the *Irish Nation* and the *Gaelic American*?

12. What paper did James Daly edit when he co-founded the Land League (1879)?

13. What is the oldest newspaper in the Republic?

14. Who edited *An Claideamh Soluis* from 1903 to 1909?

15. Who founded and edited the *Shan Van Vocht*?

Answers on page 79

1. Caendruim was the ancient name of which Co. West-meath meeting-place?

2. What was a 'ceis'?

3. Which Annals commence in 1092 and conclude in 1326?

4. On which historic site were the kings and chiefs of the O'Donnell clan inaugurated?

5. What was a 'cumal'?

6. What were stored in dwellings in leather satchels hung on pegs or racks round the walls, the contents being marked on the exterior?

7. Name the sixth-century manuscript which gives the legendary origin of many place-names.

8. Which of the Annals was transcribed by Feardomh-nach in A.D. 807?

9. What was the penalty for adultery under Brehon Law?

10. Who were the Aes Dana?

11. What was a 'fuidhir'?

12. Who or what was Grey of Macha?

13. What was 'gruidean' or 'gruiten'?

14. What portion of the cost of all handicraft could the craftsman demand as payment, according to the Brehon Laws?

15. Who, according to the Book of the Dun Cow, are descended from Ham, son of Noah?

Answers on page 80

1. What battle occurred on 10 May 1318?

2. To what battle was Sir Walter Scott referring in 'Rokeby' (canto IV) when he wrote:
   'But chief arose his victor pride
   When that brave Marshal fought and died
   And Avon-Duff to ocean bore
   His billows red with Saxon gore'?

3. Who was the successful Williamite commander at Aughrim (12 July 1691)?

4. At what battle was the Duke of Schomberg killed?

5. Which High King was relaxing in his bath when a surprise attack routed his forces?

6. Who led the first Desmond Rebellion, 1569–73?

7. What battle was fought on 19 August 1504?

8. At what battle, besides the Yellow Ford, was Sir Henry Bagenal defeated by his brother-in-law, Hugh O'Neill, Earl of Tyrone?

9. What battle was fought on 8 May 1567?

10. The Battle of Clontarf occurred on a Good Friday; what famous battle took place on Christmas Eve?

11. Who commanded the Spanish naval force despatched to O'Neill and O'Donnell in 1601?

12. At what battle on 8 August 1647 did Col Michael Jones' Parliamentarians defeat Preston's Confederates?

13. Who was defeated in the Curlew Mountains by Brian of the Battle-Axes O'Rourke on 15 August 1599?

14. What battle in A.D. 284 at Skreen, Co. Meath spelt disaster for the Fianna?

Answers on page 80

1. Which Wiltshire-based Irishman had the following penned in his honour (c. 1830):
   'I'm told dear — your lays are sung
   (Can it be true, you lucky man?)
   By moonlight in the Persian tongue
   Along the streets of Isaphan'?

2. What occurred in Mayo on 21 August 1879?

3. What organisation was modelled on the (Belgian) Boerenbond Belge?

4. Who was released from Armagh prison on humanitarian grounds on 30 April 1980?

5. Horace Hone (1756–1825) specialised in which particular field?

6. Which artist was responsible for the Bianconi 'Car Travelling' prints which form an invaluable historical record?

7. Who wrote the poem 'The Municipal Gallery Re-Visited'?

8. Which Milesian prince is believed to have composed our earliest poetry?

9. Which Irishman challenged Lord Jeffrey to a duel in 1806, because of an unfavourable review by Jeffrey of his early poetry?

10. Who established the Thomas Davis Lectures on Radio Eireann in 1953?

11. Although Thomas J. Kiernan served with distinction in the Diplomatic Service from 1941 to 1964, his wife was even more famous. Who was she?

Answers on page 81

1. Of what was Dr Walter Wade appointed first Curator in March 1795?

2. Marconi established a radio station in Ireland in 1902 with the call sign 'GCK'. 'G' was for Great Britain but what did 'CK' stand for?

3. For whom was the twelfth-century reliquary, the Cross of Cong, made?

4. For whom did Arthur Young become land-agent (1777–9)?

5. Who wrote *The Political Economy of Ireland* (1691)?

6. Name the Irishman who during the last century was a recognised authority on terrestrial magnetism.

7. Which Archbishop of Dublin was murdered by followers of Silken Thomas?

8. Musician and antiquarian Edward Bunting (1773–1843) was organist at which Dublin church?

9. Name the sculptor of the Carolan monument erected in St Patrick's Cathedral, Dublin, in 1824.

10. What product of the Dun Emer Guild can be seen in Dail Eireann?

11. Whom did Bishop O'Dwyer of Limerick describe in 1890 as 'dishonest' and 'a coward'?

12. Who was Ceann Comhairle of Dail Eireann from 1922 to 1932?

13. What did the Delamain factory produce in Dublin between 1753 and 1770?

14. Who scripted the 1951 Irish-made film *Return to Glenascaul*?

15. Whom did Daniel Kelly kill in 1583?

Answers on page 81

1. Who established the Presbyterian Remonstrant Assembly in 1829?

2. Which Bishop of Emly was hanged by Ireton in Limerick (31 October 1651)?

3. To what religious order did Papal Nuncio David Wolfe belong (arrived in 1561)?

4. Who was Church of Ireland Archbishop of Armagh and Primate until 1969?

5. What position did Mateo de Ovideo receive in 1600?

6. Whom did the Third Lateran Council appoint Papal Legate to Ireland in 1179?

7. What noted scholar was dismissed by the bishops from his post as Professor of Irish at Maynooth in 1909?

8. Where was the first Franciscan house of Observants founded in 1433?

9. Whose first Irish foundations were established at Youghal and Cork between 1224 and 1230?

10. In what famous church will you find the so-called 'Tomb of the Good Woman's Son'?

11. Where was the 1850 Catholic Synod of Bishops held?

12. What famous nineteenth-century Catholic bishop served in the Spanish Army during the Peninsular War?

13. Where did the Dominican Observants establish their first priory in 1426?

14. Whom did Pope Celestine send to Ireland in A.D. 431?

15. Over what Synod did Laurence O'Toole preside in 1179?

1. Under what name was Mrs Liam Ua Buachalla internationally known?

2. Name the grand-niece of Michael Collins who was elected TD for Dublin North in 1981.

3. Who was known as 'The Nun of Kenmare'?

4. Which singer-pianist who died in 1979 was the first female singer with the Roy Fox band, and also performed with the Jack Hylton and Phil Murtagh bands?

5. Who was the first woman president of the Irish Trades Union Congress?

6. Where was soprano Margaret Burke-Sheridan born?

7. By which name is Mrs R. H. Sturgeon who died in 1808 better known in Irish history?

8. Which nineteenth-century soprano was known as 'The Swan of Eireann'?

9. Name the Boyle, Co. Roscommon-born teacher and female emancipationist who worked tirelessly on behalf of her adopted India.

10. Which artist was, in her 100th year, invited to exhibit at the first Exhibition of Naive Art, held in London 1979?

11. Who, through her chairmanship of the Irish Red Cross since its inception in 1938, was in 1978 presented with the Society's highest award — the Henri Dunant Medal?

12. Which poetess did Seamus MacManus marry shortly before her death?

13. Mrs Anne Dickson was the first woman to lead a political party in Ireland. Name the party.

Answers on page 82

1. Which famous teacher and abbot died of the plague at Clonard on 12 December 549?

2. Where did the English monk, St Berchert, found a monastery in the eighth century?

3. Which Leinster saint is reputed to have lived to the age of one hundred and twenty and is associated with legends of an otter and of a blackbird?

4. Sherkin Island, Co. Cork, was the birthplace of which saint?

5. The sixth of June is the feast-day of which Galway-born abbot who numbered Brendan of Clonfert and Colman of Munster among his disciples?

6. Which ascetic who died in A.D. 650 experienced visions of heaven and hell while in a state of trance and inspired Dante's *Inferno*?

7. Which Co. Clare-born saint, renowned as a bee-keeper, established a convent at Ballyvourney, Co. Cork?

8. The fifteenth of January is the feast-day of which Waterford-born saint who founded a Co. Limerick convent?

9. The Domhnach Airgid or Silver Shrine contains the bones of which saint, regarded as one of the earliest miracle-workers?

10. Which Co. Tipperary abbot is believed to have contributed to the demise of Tara by cursing it and its rulers?

11. Which Scottish islands, off Ross Shire, are named in honour of an Irish saint?

Answers on page 83

1. Which President of University College Dublin was a world authority on quaternions?

2. Whose major nineteenth-century work was the Geological Survey of Ireland?

3. In what branch of knowledge was Edward Joshua Cooper noted?

4. Who held chairs of National Economics (from 1926) and Political Economy (from 1930) at UCD until 1961?

5. Who edited the letters of John O'Donovan on Irish topography into fifty volumes?

6. What had Roderic O'Flaherty's *Ogygia* (published in 1685) as its subject?

7. Which Limerick historian was a medical authority on head injuries, his experience gained through treating victims of faction-fighting?

8. Which famous Irish scholar translated the works of Hans Christian Andersen into Irish?

9. Who published the first translation of 'Cuirt a' Mhean Oiche' ('The Midnight Court'), in 1926?

10. Which famous scholar was principal of Marlborough Street Training College in Dublin (1874–1914)?

11. Karl Marx was described by the Webbs as the disciple of which pioneering Irish economist?

12. Who became famous for his eight-volume *Annales Minores*, a history of the Franciscan order?

13. Who was the author of the twelfth-century *Topographia Hiberniae*?

14. Who, while working for the Ordnance Survey, listed more than 62,000 place names?

Answers on page 83

1. Who purchased the German arms in 1914 which were landed at Howth from the *Asgard*?

2. Which one-time Minister and political leader had a grandfather who was a Young Ireland leader?

3. Who was Governor of Derry during its 105-day siege in 1689?

4. Name the adventurer who attempted to seize Dublin Castle in 1663 and kidnap the Duke of Ormond.

5. Name the HQ of the Repeal Association in the 1840s.

6. What were the Brunswick Clubs of the nineteenth century set up to oppose?

7. King James II opened the 'Patriot Parliament' of 1689. When was the next occasion on which an Irish Parliament was opened by a King?

8. The 'Doneraile Conspiracy' of 1829 provided the background to what novel?

9. Who won the Galway by-election of February 1886?

10. What paper did John Martin launch on 24 June 1848?

11. Who resigned as Minister for Education following the 'leak' of the Boundary Commission findings in 1925?

12. Which GOC in Ireland negotiated the Truce in the War of Independence with de Valera in July 1921?

13. Who was the first Rector of the Catholic University (1854)?

14. Which Irish saint founded a monastery at Luxeuil in A.D. 610?

15. In which New York borough was Eamon de Valera born?

Answers on page 84

1. How many 'Tribes of Galway' are there?

2. Name the Galway goldsmith credited with fashioning the Claddagh Ring.

3. Name the Kinvara-born poet and songwriter, author of 'The Ould Plaid Shawl', who founded the influential Southwark Irish Literary Club, London, in 1883.

4. Who in his 1939 book described the Aran Islands as 'breakwaters to the Atlantic rollers, and the twenty-seven miles is seldom smooth, an argument perhaps against a return trip in one day'?

5. St Cleran's, Co. Galway was the birthplace of which explorer in 1820?

6. The work of which Co. Galway author was chosen by UNESCO for translation into several European languages?

7. Which Mayo-born historian published a *History of Galway* in 1820?

8. The Square, Galway, was birthplace in 1911 of which military historian?

9. Which novelist was known as the 'Princess of Connemara'?

10. The Arms of which Queen adorn the Great Mace of Galway?

11. What did Galway celebrate in 1984?

12. Where is Columbus said to have worshipped before setting off on the last leg of his voyage of discovery?

13. What traditions govern the manner in which the Claddagh Ring is worn ?

Answers on page 84

1. Corkman Thomas Kirk was responsible for the ill-fated Nelson's Pillar in Dublin. What other landmark did he also design?

2. Which architect was known as 'The Wren of Ireland'?

3. Who designed the National Library of Ireland?

4. Who designed the *Titanic*?

5. Whose first commission was to design the stained-glass windows for the Honan Chapel, Cork?

6. Who won a medal for his design of the Kilkenny Design Centre?

7. Who designed Dublin's Rotunda Hospital?

8. Russborough House, Co. Wicklow, was designed by which famous architect in 1741?

9. Who designed Charlemont House, now the Municipal Gallery of Modern Art, Dublin?

10. Whose design for the Parnell Monument, Dublin, won him £5,000?

11. Trinity College Library cost £15,000 to complete. Who was its designer?

12. Who designed the Royal College of Surgeons in Dublin?

13. What Limerick bridge was designed by the brothers Pain?

14. The Church of Christ the King, Turner's Cross, Cork, was designed by which Chicago-based Irishman in 1937?

15. Who designed Cork City Hall (1935)?

Answers on page 85

1. Who, following a twenty year interval, returned to the Abbey Theatre on 31 January 1967 to play Con the Shaughran?

2. In what year was the Landlord and Tenant Act introduced, enabling tenants to purchase ground rents?

3. For whose papers did Trinity College Dublin pay £50,000 in December 1968?

4. What castle was acquired for a nominal £50 on 12 August 1967?

5. Which actress' appearance at the Mount Brandon Hotel, Tralee, was cancelled on 23 April 1967 when the local PP voiced opposition to her performance?

6. Ireland's first Honorary Citizen died on 20 January 1968. Who was he?

7. Traffic Wardens appeared on the streets of Dublin for the first time in what year?

8. When was the breathalyser test introduced?

9. Brendan Behan and Sean O'Casey died in what year?

10. Why was Oliver Goldsmith's school pulled down at Edgeworthstown, Co. Longford, on 19 July 1968?

11. In what year did Eamon de Valera defeat T. F. O' Higgins, Jack Lynch become Taoiseach and the Abbey Theatre re-open?

12. In what year did the National Gallery purchase Goya's *El Sueño* ('The Dream') for £145,000?

13. Who resigned as managing director of Comhlucht Siuicre Eireann on 19 December 1968?

14. Why was media attention focused on a CIE retirement party on 15 November 1968?

Answers on page 85

1. In what city, singing 'All Kinds of Everything', did Dana win the 1970 Eurovision Song Contest?

2. Which artist was commemorated by the issue of a centenary stamp in August 1971?

3. In what year were radio licences abolished?

4. Name the Soviet composer who received an Honorary Doctorate in Music from Trinity College Dublin on 6 July 1972.

5. What Irish hotel became, on 6 November 1975, the first ever recipient of the Egon Ronay Gold Plate Award?

6. Who were married in Limerick Prison on 24 January 1978?

7. In what year did RTE's Radio 2 open?

8. What former political opponents received the Freedom of the City of Dublin on 7 March 1975?

9. What happened to all branches of Power's supermarket chain on 23 May 1972?

10. When did the Ferenka plant close in Limerick with the loss of fourteen hundred jobs?

11. Who in 1977 became the first member of the Jewish Community to be elected chairman of Dublin County Council?

12. What Department did Charles Haughey abolish shortly after election as Taoiseach (11 December 1979)?

13. Which ballad-singer died, aged 69, on 12 February 1971?

14. On his visit to Ireland in 1970 what graveyard, containing the reputed grave of his Quaker ancestors, did President Nixon visit?

Answers on page 86

1. What was 'A Sense of Ireland'?

2. What country won the 1981 Eurovision Song Contest at the RDS, Dublin?

3. The Unionist Party in Northern Ireland and which political party in the South refused the invitation to participate in the New Ireland Forum?

4. Who was the star attraction at the concert at Slane Castle, Co. Meath attended by 50,000 on 8 July 1984?

5. What liquidation was announced on 14 November 1984?

6. What title did Gerry Fitt assume on his elevation to the peerage in 1983?

7. What Co. Clare pub was sold for a reputed £1,000,000 in June 1983?

8. In what year was the first weld made in the Cork-Dublin gas pipeline?

9. What college, with *Hiems transit* ('Winter passes') for its motto, celebrated its bicentenary on 5 March 1982?

10. Who 'passed-out' for the first time on 29 October 1981?

11. Who was chairman of the Tribunal which investigated the Whiddy Island Disaster (reported on 25 August 1980)?

12. Who was appointed to chair the Commission on Taxation (established on 4 February 1980)?

13. Whom did Padraic White succeed as Managing Director of the IDA on 19 February 1981?

14. In what year did the National Concert Hall open?

15. Who in September 1982 founded the New Ireland Organisation?

Answers on page 86

1. Who founded the Christian Democratic Party in the 1960s?

2. Who founded the Ulster Farmers' and Labourers' Union and Compulsory Purchase Association?

3. Who founded the Irish Christian Front in 1935?

4. What organisation did Charles Hubert Oldham found in 1886?

5. What organisation was founded by John Dillon and Justin McCarthy in March 1891?

6. Who founded the Home Government Association in 1870?

7. What literary magazine was founded by Sean O'Faolain in 1940?

8. What organisation established the Central Relief Committee in 1846?

9. What did John Stearne or Sterne found in 1660?

10. Who founded the Irish Socialist Republican Party?

11. Who founded the Irish Wheelchair Association?

12. Of what is Thomas Prior regarded as founder?

13. Who were the co-founders of *Irish Historical Studies*?

14. What political party was co-founded in the 1930s by Frank MacDermott?

15. Who founded the first 'Lying-In Hospital' in these islands?

Answers on page 87

1. By what Irish title did Domhnall Ua Buachalla hold office as Governor-General of the Free State?

2. By what other name is the 'Act for the speedy and effectual reducing of the rebels in His Majesty's kingdom of Ireland' known?

3. What famous teacher was sometimes known as 'Sean a' Chota'?

4. What was the surname of the seventeenth-century Barons of Howth?

5. Whose name was originally Crimthann?

6. Who used the pen-name 'An Seabhac' ('The Hawk')?

7. By what other name is Mrs Padraig O'Guithin popularly known?

8. By what nickname was Thomas Butler, Eighth Earl of Ormond known?

9. What is the Irish title for the 'Book of Invasions'?

10. What was the family name of Lord Charlemont?

11. Who was known as the 'Sham Squire'?

12. To whom was Mrs Matilda Wilson, who died on 18 March 1849, first married?

13. By what name were the schools of the 'Incorporated Society for Promoting English Schools' known?

14. What title was held by 'Silken' Thomas FitzGerald for most of his life?

15. What name is given to the announcement of Gladstone's conversion to Home Rule in December 1885?

Answers on page 87

1. Who was crowned King of England in Christ Church, Dublin, on 24 May 1487?

2. Who on 6 September 1862 became the first Director of the National Gallery?

3. Name the Cork-born but Kerry-based journalist and politician who led the 'Plan of Campaign' in the 1880s.

4. What constituency did Captain W. H. O'Shea first represent?

5. What Dublin station was designed by William Deane Butler in 1844?

6. What was found at Reerasta Rath, Co. Limerick, in 1867?

7. In what year was the Arts Council established?

8. Who chaired the Irish Convention, 1917–18?

9. Which Attorney-General earned the sobriquet 'Peter the Packer' for his selection of sectarian juries?

10. What order founded Athassel Priory, Co. Tipperary, towards the end of the twelfth century, (later the largest medieval monastic complex in Ireland)?

11. What was the name given to the part-time constabulary who patrolled Irish roads in the early nineteenth century?

12. Who arrived at Sheephaven Bay, Co. Donegal, in July 1642?

13. What in 1863 did John Caldwell Bloomfield, David McBirney and Robert Williams Armstrong found?

14. Which important historical character whose misfortune commenced in 1803, died impoverished on 18 September 1851?

Answers on page 88

1. What poem ends 'O people that I have loved shall we not answer together'?

2. Who wrote the lines:
   'I heard the Poor Old Woman say:
   "At break of day the fowler came
   And took my blackbirds from their songs
   Who loved me well thro' shame and blame" '?

3. Who wrote 'The Red Flag'?

4. Whose poetry was published as *The Four Winds of Eireann* (1902)?

5. What has 'The Blacksmith of Limerick' as subject?

6. Who wrote 'Lament on the Death of John O'Mahony'?

7. What epic poem begins, 'Crom Cruach and his sub-gods twelve'?

8. Who wrote the 1798 ballad 'Kelly of Killann'?

9. Who wrote the 'Lament for Owen Roe O'Neill'?

10. According to Florence M. Wilson, who was the man they hanged at Downpatrick Gaol?

11. Which poet from exile asked, 'Am I remembered in Erin?'?

12. What poem was written by Richard D'Alton Williams to commemorate the victory of the united clans of Munster over the Anglo-Normans at Thurles, Co. Tipperary in 1190?

13. Who wrote 'The Famine Year'?

14. Which poet willed that his ashes be scattered over the River Erne?

15. How did Peadar Kearney, author of the National Anthem, earn a living?

Answers on page 88

1. Who became owner of the *Nation* in 1855?

2. What organisation published the *Gael*?

3. What Irish-American paper was edited by Patrick Ford?

4. Who edited *Gaelic American* from 1903 until the 1920s?

5. What paper did John Mitchel found in 1848?

6. What paper was founded 'To create and foster public opinion, and make it racy of the soil'?

7. By what name is the old *Skibbereen Eagle* now known?

8. What paper was founded by Richard Barrett in 1828 to assist Daniel O'Connell?

9. Who sold the *Irishman*, the *Flag of Ireland* and the *Shamrock* to Parnell in 1881?

10. Who published and edited *Sinn Fein* from 1906 onwards?

11. Who edited the *Irish Homestead*?

12. What paper was at various times edited by Eoin MacNeill and Patrick Pearse?

13. Who was the first editor of the *United Ireland*, Parnell's newspaper (1881–90)?

14. What paper was founded and edited by D. P. Moran?

15. What paper was founded by Henry Joy in 1737?

Answers on page 89

1. Name the bishop-general hanged by Cromwellians after the Battle of Scarifhollis (1650).

2. Who defeated the Earl of Desmond at Affane, Co. Waterford, 1 February 1565?

3. Where did Sir George Carew defeat the O'Sullivans in 1602?

4. Whose claims to land in 1568 helped to foment the first Munster Rebellion?

5. Who captured Dublin in A.D. 1000?

6. Who led the besieging force at Limerick, 4 June 1651?

7. Where did the Battle of Dun Bolg take place in A.D. 598?

8. Who killed Edward Bruce at the Battle of Faughart, 14 October 1318?

9. Which family was responsible for the death of James Fitzmaurice Fitzgerald in 1579?

10. Who defeated the High King at the Battle of Cuildreimhne?

11. Which Catholic Archbishop of Armagh was killed in battle against Sir Richard Bingham on 23 June 1593?

12. Who defeated the King of Tara in battle at Mag Lena, A.D. 907?

13. Who was killed by Sergeant Milborne on 7–8 May 1597?

14. Whose soldiers destroyed Cashel with great brutality during the Confederate Wars?

15. Which Irish leader defeated the Norse at the Battle of Sulchoit (modern Solohead, Co. Tipperary)?

Answers on page 89

1. Which Northern Ireland PM signed the Sunningdale Agreement?

2. Who was the first Governor-General of Northern Ireland?

3. Who succeeded Lord Brookeborough as PM of Northern Ireland?

4. Who, along with Joseph Devlin, was the first Nationalist to enter the Northern Ireland Parliament (28 April 1925)?

5. Who was the last PM of Northern Ireland?

6. Who was 'Father of the Senate' of Northern Ireland, 1921–4?

7. Who was the only Catholic appointed to the Northern Ireland Cabinet?

8. Who was appointed on 28 August 1969 to monitor Northern Ireland's Reform Programme?

9. To what organisation did Rudyard Kipling contribute in 1913?

10. How many Ulster counties did T. C. Agar-Robertes propose should be excluded from Home Rule?

11. Who, on 27 August 1969, headed the tribunal to inquire into Northern Ireland disturbances ?

12. Who led the Commonwealth Labour Party until 1942?

13. What political party was founded in Northern Ireland by W. J. Stewart in 1938?

14. Who was leader of the Northern Ireland Senate from 1937 to 1943?

15. Where were People's Democracy marchers attacked by a mob in January 1969?

Answers on page 90

1. Of what county was Sir William Wilde, doctor, scholar and father of Oscar, a native?

2. Where was Mother Mary Aikenhead, founder of the Irish Sisters of Charity, born in 1787?

3. The great Franciscan scholar Luke Wadding was born in what city on 16 October 1658?

4. Where was the philosopher Bishop George Berkeley born on 12 March 1685?

5. Who was born, son of a coach-maker, at 44 Stafford Street, Dublin, on 20 June 1763 (the street now bears his name)?

6. Faughart, Co. Louth, is believed to be the birth-place of which saint?

7. In what city was Napper Tandy born?

8. Where were the brothers Alexander Martin (historian and politician) and T. D. Sullivan (politician and poet) born?

9. Where was William Brown, 'Father of the Argentinian Navy', born in 1777?

10. In what county was the bard Turlough Carolan born?

11. Where was James Stephens, founder of the IRB, born in 1825?

12. Leading Unionist Sir Henry Carson was born in what city?

13. Sculptor Oliver Sheppard was a native of what county?

14. In what city was Erskine Childers, fourth President of Ireland, born on 11 December 1905?

15. Where was Patrick Sarsfield born?

Answers on page 90

1. Which fifth-century poet is regarded as the last great bard of pagan Ireland?

2. Who, in an early ninth-century poem, was Pangur?

3. Which seventeenth-century bard composed 'Ode to the Maguires'?

4. Who wrote 'The Cup of O'Hara' (written in Irish)?

5. Which poet addressed lines to his friend commencing:
   'O'Tuomy! you boast yourself handy
   At selling good ale and bright brandy . . .'?

6. In the J. J. Callanan poem who is reminiscing:
   'I'd dance without tiring
   From morning till even',
   And the goal-ball I'd strike
   To the lightning of Heaven'.

7. In which famous poem is there an encounter with
   'a hag of hideous guise' whose 'shape with age and ague shook,
   The plain she scoured with glowering look'?

8. Which poet writes of 'playing music to empty pockets'?

9. Who wrote a poem entitled 'On the Death of Dr Swift'?

10. What, according to Goldsmith's 'Deserted Village', 'once destroyed can never be supplied'?

11. Who wrote the poem 'The Friar of Orders Grey'?

12. Who wrote 'Rodney's Lament'?

13. Who 'lost his watch in Doneraile' and cursed the village in a famous satire?

14. Who wrote 'The Wake of William Orr'?

Answers on page 91

1. Who represented the Free State at Washington, 1924–7?

2. Who preceded Parnell as leader of the Home Rule Party?

3. Who was Minister for Finance, 1957–65?

4. Which Taoiseach signed the Sunningdale Agreement?

5. How many deputies were elected to the Free State Parliament in 1921?

6. Who was Minister for Justice, 1933–9?

7. Whom did Daniel O'Connell defeat in the Clare by-election, 1828?

8. What was the original name of the party more popularly known as Fine Gael, from 1933?

9. Which Cavan-Monaghan TD died on hunger strike on 2 August 1981?

10. Who has been the longest-serving leader of the Labour Party?

11. What political leader had a mother who was secretary to George Bernard Shaw?

12. Who won the North Roscommon by-election for Sinn Fein in 1917?

13. Who was first President of Fine Gael (September 1933)?

14. What organisation was founded by members of Griffith's Cumann na nGaedheal to protest against the King's visit to Ireland?

15. Who was Minister for External Affairs, 1954–7?

Answers on page 91

1. What did Fr Patrick Ahern establish in 1968?

2. Who founded the short-lived Ralahine Agricultural and Manufacturing Co-Operative (Co. Clare)?

3. What body was founded by Irish landlords for their own protection in the 1880s?

4. Who founded the Ulster Tenant Right Association, 1847?

5. What did Charles Gavan Duffy and Frederick Lucas establish in August 1850?

6. What theatre did Alan Simpson and Carolyn Swift found in 1953?

7. Name the co-founders of the *United Irishman* and Cumann na nGaedheal, 1899–1900.

8. Whose famous letter to the Duke of Leinster outlined a scheme for National Education in 1831?

9. Who founded the Independent Orange Order in 1902?

10. Who founded the 1913 Club in 1957?

11. Who founded the Pre-Cursor society in 1838?

12. What did Fr O'Shea and Fr Keeffe establish in Callan in 1849?

13. Who founded the Employers' Federation (later FUE)?

14. What Irish town was built by Charles Strickland to spite his neighbours?

15. Who founded the People's Rights Association in 1897?

Answers on page 92

1. Who was the first Irishman to become Poet Laureate?

2. Which future British PM was wounded in the thigh in a duel with Lord Castlereagh on Wimbledon Common in September 1809?

3. Name the Dublin-born actor (d. 1721) who is commemorated by an annual London Bridge-Chelsea Thames race.

4. London's Royal Albert Hall was designed by which Belfastman in 1865?

5. Who saved Goldsmith from eviction by personally conveying the manuscript of *The Vicar of Wakefield* to the publisher from whom he received a £60 cheque?

6. Name the Limerick-born Archbishop of Armagh who escaped from the Tower of London but was recaptured and died there (14 October 1585).

7. Which Co. Kilkenny man was, as Master of the Mint, responsible for the 'Godless florin'?

8. Of which county was Field Marshal Alexander of Tunis a native?

9. Which actor, born of Ulster parents, caused William Pitt to move an adjournment motion so that the MPs might see him in the title role of *Hamlet*?

10. Dublin-born Edmund Malone (1741–1812) was considered the leading authority on what subject?

11. Which famous Irishman occupied Apsley House, near Hyde Park Corner, London?

12. Which Irish illustrator was responsible for *Punch*'s original and famous cover?

Answers on page 92

1. Of which Cork-born artist was 'Alfred Croquis' the pseudonym?

2. Who was the Catholic bishop on whom the 'Bard of Armagh' was based?

3. Who was made 'Head Pacificator' by Daniel O'Connell specifically to quell faction-fighting?

4. What was the pen-name of Lady Wilde?

5. By which name is Hazel Trudeau, who died in 1935, better known?

6. Which physician and poet wrote under the pseudonym 'The Kilkenny Man'?

7. Who was 'Leo', one of the Fenian poets?

8. Name 'The Belfastman' who was actually a native of Ballincollig, Co. Cork.

9. 'William of Munster' wrote 'The Moon Behind the Hill' as he gazed through the bars of Clonmel Jail. Who was he?

10. Who wrote poetry for the *Nation* under the pen-name 'Eva'?

11. Who was 'Sliabh Cuilinn' of the *Nation*?

12. Who was the 'Bard of the Lee'?

13. Who died bearing the title 'Baron of Duncairn'?

14. By which name is Ellen Hanly better known?

15. What name was Robert Emmet using at the time of his arrest?

Answers on page 93

1. In what year was Clann na Poblachta formed?

2. The celebrated 'Doneraile Conspiracy' trial took place in what year?

3. The sixth and seventh of January of what year became known as 'The Night of the Big Wind'?

4. In what year did forty eight people lose their lives during a showing of *The Ten Commandments* in Drumcollogher, Co. Limerick?

5. On 27 May of what year did Irish Sea Airways (now known as Aer Lingus) have its first commercial flight?

6. On 1 September of what year was Ireland's oldest newspaper, *The Belfast Newsletter*, founded?

7. Irish coinage depicting animals and fish was first issued in what year?

8. In what year did the *Princess Victoria* sink off Co. Down, with the loss of one hundred and thirty lives?

9. On 1 August of what year did Patrick Pearse deliver his oration at the graveside of O'Donovan Rossa?

10. When was Kevin Barry executed?

11. What year saw the death of John M. Synge and the formation of the ITGWU?

12. In what year did James Joyce die and Irish Shipping Ltd come into existence?

13. In what year did Galway Corporation demolish the Claddagh and Patricia Lynch publish *The Turfcutter's Donkey*?

14. In what year did the death of Thomas Davis occur and Wallace's *Maritana* have its first performance?

Answers on page 93

1. Where in Dublin did the National Maternity Hospital open on 17 March 1894?

2. Where did the copper miners who worked in Allihies, Co. Cork, come from?

3. Where were the terminal points of the first Irish canal?

4. Where was the Irish section of the National Agricultural Labourers' Union founded in 1873?

5. Where did John Philip Sousa give two concerts on 13 February 1911?

6. Where was Sir Ernest Shackleton born?

7. Where will you find the 'Devil's Bastion'?

8. Where did the Dublin Society open its first Gardens?

9. Where did Edmund Supple and his wife 'whom love binds in one' build a famous fortified house?

10. Where was Fastnet Lighthouse originally built?

11. Where were the first reports of moving statues on 14 March 1985?

12. Where did John Redmond deliver the speech in September 1914 which led to the split in the Irish Volunteers?

13. Where can be seen a figure representing Eire, bearing a copy of the Catholic Emancipation Act?

14. Where would you find the 'Rubrics'?

15. Where was St Colmcille born?

Answers on page 94

1. What organisation was founded in 1921 by Sinn Fein to distribute aid to Republicans?

2. Who led the RIC mutiny at Listowel, Co. Kerry?

3. Which IRA general was freed by the British as a condition for the Truce of 11 July 1921?

4. Which British general was captured by the IRA on 26 June 1920?

5. Who was the author of *The Reality of the Anglo-Irish War 1919–21* (1974).

6. Who was the IRA Chief of Staff in early 1919?

7. Who led the attack on the Shropshire Light Infantry in Fermoy on 7 September 1919?

8. What was Kevin Barry studying at UCD?

9. What was the only military barracks captured by the IRA?

10. What was the title of Ernie O'Malley's book on his career during the War of Independence?

11. Who led the rescue of Sean Hogan from the Cork-Dublin train at Knocklong, Co. Limerick?

12. On what Dublin Street was Sean Treacy killed in a gun-battle?

13. What was the significance of the taking of Shantonagh, Co. Monaghan, RIC Barracks by the IRA on 14 February 1920?

14. Which IRA commandant served in Mesopotamia before returning in 1919 to inflict two heavy defeats on Crown forces during the War of Independence?

15. On what date was the Anglo-Irish Treaty signed in London in 1921?

Answers on page 95

1. Who became famous for discovering a new technique for operations on the prostate?

2. Who made the independent discovery of Ohm's Law?

3. What did Peter Woulfe (c. 1727–1803) invent?

4. Who invented the dirigible torpedo?

5. What optician manufactured the reflecting and refracting equipment for observatories at Armagh and Dunsink?

6. For what was Edward Hallaran Bennett distinguished?

7. For what did Dr John McDonnell become famous on 1 January 1847?

8. Who, in 1681, discovered vascularity of the lens of the eye while operating on an elephant which had died?

9. Who invented the buckled plate (1852)?

10. What did John Howard Kyan invent in 1832?

11. What was known as 'Leviathan'?

12. Who was the scientist responsible for *The Industrial Resources of Ireland* (1844)?

13. Who pioneered ultra-rapid cinematography?

14. Which Belfast-born scientist known for his discovery of the Second Law of Thermodynamics, also made valuable contributions in the areas of electricity and submarine telegraphy?

15. The work of which Belfast-born physical chemist, who died in 1885, resulted in the liquefaction of the permanent gases?

Answers on page 95

1. Who was the Gaelic god of medicine?

2. Who were Brian, Iuchar and Iucharba?

3. Of whom was 'Balor of the Evil Eye' leader?

4. Who slew 'Balor of the Evil Eye'?

5. With whom did Deirdre elope?

6. What was the fate of Deirdre when her lover was treacherously slain on the orders of Conor Mac Nessa?

7. How did Fionn cause the death of Diarmuid?

8. Who was the wandering architect believed to have been responsible for the building of the Round Towers?

9. What was 'Gorm Glas'?

10. Which beautiful goddess possessed three colourful birds which could lull the sick to sleep?

11. Who was the wife of Manannan Mac Lir who fell in love with Cuchulainn?

12. What was the name of Medb's husband in the *Tain*?

13. Who was the druid to Conor Mac Nessa whose spell allowed the capture of the Sons of Usnach?

14. What was the favourite pastime of Cet, champion of Connaught?

15. What was 'Freagarthach'?

Answers on page 96

1. What body held its inaugural meeting on 1 July 1893?

2. In what year was the Disestablishment Act for the Church of Ireland enacted?

3. What mutiny commenced on 28 June 1920?

4. In what year was the Irish Medical Association founded?

5. The last of the Blasket islanders were re-settled on the mainland in what year?

6. What was first heard on 2 April 1972?

7. In what year was Ireland's first rail link from Dublin to Kingstown opened?

8. What did a meeting in Co. Mayo on 20 April 1879 help launch?

9. For what was a charter issued on 2 September 1850?

10. What event was held for the first time from 21 October to 4 November 1951?

11. In what year did Margaret Browne become the first Ban-Garda?

12. What famous treasure trove was unearthed in February 1896?

13. Which famous Irishman was executed on 1 July 1681?

14. Which religious organisation made its first Irish appearance in Belfast on 4 May 1880?

15. Name the unique railway which opened on 29 February 1888.

Answers on page 96

1. Which Cork-born artist who died on 22 February 1806 is buried in St Paul's Cathedral, London?

2. What caused the death of Cormac Mac Art?

3. Buried in Westminster Abbey in August 1822, of whom was it said 'He first cut his country's throat, and then his own'?

4. Where in London are buried novelist Lady Morgan and folklorist Thomas Crofton Croker?

5. What Dublin landmark did Jimmy O'Dea describe in 1953 as 'The Tomb of the Unknown Gurrier'?

6. Thomas Moore is buried in which cemetery?

7. Where is the composer Michael William Balfe buried?

8. Where is Brendan Behan buried?

9. St Michan's in Dublin is the resting place of which United Irishman who died in prison in September 1798?

10. Where was William Burke (partner of William Hare) executed for murder on 28 January 1829?

11. Where is Isaac Butt buried?

12. Where did George Bernard Shaw will that his ashes be scattered?

13. Where is John Millington Synge buried?

14. Meningitis was the cause of death on 30 November 1900 of which Irishman who is buried in Pere Lachaise, Paris?

15. Where, shortly after re-election as MP for Tipperary, did John Mitchel die?

Answers on page 97

1. How many round towers are there at Clonmacnoise?

2. Who supervised the Valuation of Ireland in the nineteenth century?

3. Who issued the 'No Tax Manifesto' in the *Freeman's Journal* on 17 February 1887?

4. What important society, still active, was founded in Cork in 1892?

5. Gerry Fitt was a member of which political party before co-founding the SDLP?

6. What was the monetary qualification for the franchise after 1829?

7. In what year did the outbreak of myxomatosis occur: 1952, 1953 or 1954?

8. Which family founded the Cuala Press?

9. Which poet, born at Greenock, Scotland, became Irish Ambassador to Italy in 1958?

10. Of whom did the Four Masters say, he died 'without penance . . . as his evil deeds deserved'?

11. Who succeeded Thomas MacDonagh as Lecturer in English at UCD in 1916?

12. What colour clothing, favoured in Gaelic society, was forbidden by a law of 1536?

13. Who was Cuchulainn's wife?

14. What word was first used in print in the *Daily Mail* on 13 December 1880?

15. Who organised the Irish Military College in 1926?

Answers on page 97

1. In 1829 at Donaghadee, Co. Down, John Cochrane paid his workers for 'sprigging' or 'flowering'. What was it?

2. Belgian Gaspar Huybrechts produced the earliest known Irish specimen of what at Kilkenny in 1645?

3. Who was 'Imperatoris Scotorum'?

4. Pope Clement III canonised which Irish saint in 1190?

5. Among the gifts presented at the consecration of which church in 1157 were 120 ounces of gold, a hundred and forty cattle, a chalice and vestments?

6. Which city in 1851 housed the first menswear tailoring factory in Ireland?

7. Jack Clarke was the first to exploit the fabric export market using native cloths. What label did he use?

8. Which Belfast-born poet and antiquarian, knighted in 1878, was the first Deputy-Keeper of the Public Records in Ireland?

9. In what Co. Tipperary town did St Cronan found a monastery in the seventh century?

10. What castle has been home of Edmund Spenser, an estate office and printing works, a police barracks, and is now a museum?

11. Where do Martello towers take their name from?

12. Name the sculptor of the Charles Kickham monument in Tipperary town.

13. What body took over the functions of the Poor Law Commissioners in 1872?

14. Who became the Lord Deputy on 17 November 1657?

Answers on page 98

1. What was the first play in Irish to be given a professional production?

2. What local authority set the precedent for the managerial system of local government?

3. What was the first car to be widely seen in Ireland?

4. Who was the first Commissioner of the Irish Civic Guards?

5. What was the theme of Daniel O'Connell's first major public speech (13 January 1800)?

6. Who in 1767 became the first fully-resident Lord Lieutenant?

7. What made their first official appearance on 1 September 1969?

8. Which was the first Union workhouse in Dublin to open?

9. What event was held for the first time on 15 April 1864?

10. Who was the first Chief Justice of the Free State?

11. What word is first recorded in Irish history in connection with the death of Risteard Mag Raghnaill (1405)?

12. How did John Kearney create history in 1571?

13. Who was the first woman in the Senate of the National University of Ireland 1909–24?

14. What was the first ship built for Irish Shipping Ltd in 1948?

15. Who is credited with the invention of musical glasses?

Answers on page 98

1. What were 'fulachta fiadha'?

2. What was a 'ramut'?

3. What is the derivation of the word 'bothar' (road)?

4. What was a 'meisin'?

5. What district of Western Scotland owes its name to the colonising Irish?

6. What term has been given to the period A.D. 875–915?

7. What was the 'aireacht'?

8. What was an 'anradh' or 'anroth'?

9. What did the ancient legal term 'anarra' mean?

10. What name was given to the voluminous cloak common to both sexes, worn over a shirt or tunic, secured by a brooch or fibula?

11. What name was given to the area in which wine was stored in a monastery?

12. What was a 'crotal' or 'crohal'?

13. What major difference separated Irish druids from their Gaulish counterparts?

14. At what age according to Brehon Law could a young man give legal evidence?

15. What was 'fingal'?

Answers on page 99

1. Which of the Fianna was noted for the love spot on his cheek?

2. Who was the speediest runner of the Fianna?

3. Which member of the Fianna, regarded as a buffoon, was also bald?

4. The mother of which member of the Fianna was changed by a druid into a deer?

5. On what hill did Fionn build his palace?

6. Which giant of the Tuatha de Danann kidnapped fifteen of the Fianna on his magic horse?

7. Which king had the Fianna as his reserve army?

8. What was the surname of Diarmuid?

9. What was the relationship between Fionn and Diarmuid?

10. What was Fionn's name as a boy?

11. Where was Fionn secretly reared?

12. Which of the Fianna had only one eye?

13. Whose daughter was Grainne, Fionn's betrothed?

14. Who was the father of Niamh Cinn Oir?

15. What was the motto of the Fianna?

Answers on page 100

1. The rods of what tree were used by the druids in divination?

2. What was 'tearmann'?

3. From what wood were chariot-shafts manufactured?

4. What wood was used principally in house and fence-construction?

5. How did the Irish and Roman forms of tonsure differ?

6. What were the three orders of the Irish saints?

7. In monasteries or ecclesiastical schools how many grades or orders of wisdom were there?

8. When were sacred relics brought on circuit?

9. What was 'gossipred'?

10. Under Brehon Law what crime was regulated by 'eric'?

11. How was peace maintained during the Great Feis of Tara?

12. Who in a Royal household was the 'roydamna'?

13. The *Seanchus Mor* was the ancient civil law code. Name the volume which dealt with criminal law.

14. What name was given to the room in a monastery where manuscripts were written and illuminated?

15. How many years of study were necessary to attain the rank of 'ollamh' or 'learned man'?

Answers on page 100

1. Who was Chief Secretary during the 1916 Rising?

2. Which 1916 commandant served with the British Army in India?

3. Who was the first Catholic Bishop to denounce publicly General Maxwell's policy of execution of the 1916 leaders?

4. Who was responsible for the killing of Francis Sheehy-Skeffington and two journalists during the Rising?

5. Who was Under-Secretary during the 1916 Rising?

6. Who commanded the Third Battalion Irish Volunteers in the Mount Street Bridge area which inflicted the heaviest casualties on attacking forces?

7. Who commanded the Irish Volunteers at Jacob's Factory?

8. Where was the last incident of the 1916 Rising?

9. How many republicans were killed in action during the Rising?

10. Who were the first three leaders to be executed?

11. How did the text of Pearse's surrender document commence?

12. Who worked as a railway engineer in Canada, returned to fight, was wounded in 1916 and was executed in the Civil War?

13. Who was A-de-C to Joseph Plunkett in the GPO?

14. Name the bulletin circulated during the Rising which contained Pearse's first *communique* announcing the setting up of the Provisional Government.

Answers on page 101

1. Who was Northern Ireland's first Minister for Finance?

2. What office did J. M. Andrews hold, 1937–41?

3. Who was the last Northern Ireland Minister for Finance before Direct Rule (1972)?

4. Who was Northern Ireland Minister for Home Affairs, 1959–63?

5. What was the largest number of seats held by the Unionist Party from 1921 to 1972?

6. What was the largest number of seats held by the Nationalist Party from 1921 to 1972?

7. How many seats did the Alliance Party hold in the Northern Ireland Assembly, 1973?

8. How many seats did the SDLP hold in the Northern Ireland Assembly in 1973?

9. What party held the largest single number of seats in the Northern Ireland Assembly?

10. How many seats did the Northern Ireland Labour Party win in the general election for Stormont in 1969?

11. What Ministry did Harry Midgley hold in Northern Ireland government, 1945–51?

12. Who was the first Northern Ireland Minister for Agriculture?

13. Who was the first Governor of Northern Ireland?

14. Who was deputy to Chief Executive Brian Faulkner in the Northern Ireland Executive?

15. Who was the first holder of the Community Relations portfolio at Stormont?

Answers on page 101

1. What new Department was created in July 1959?

2. Who was Tanaiste in the second Inter-Party government, 1954–7?

3. Who became Minister for Education on 13 July 1966?

4. Who was Tanaiste to Sean Lemass from 1959 to 1965?

5. Who was Tanaiste from 1965 to 1969?

6. Who was Tanaiste to Jack Lynch from 1969 to 1973?

7. Who, during 1976–7, was first Minister for Lands and then Minister for Fisheries?

8. Who was Minister for Local Government from 1959 to 1966?

9. Who was Minister for Justice from 1965 to 1968?

10. What office did Sean Flanagan hold from 1966 to 1969?

11. Who was Minister for Local Government from May 1970 to March 1973?

12. Who was the first Tanaiste to Charles Haughey (1979)?

13. What new Department was created under Taoiseach Liam Cosgrave in the National Coalition Government (1973–7)?

14. Who was Attorney-General in the Fianna Fail administration 1977–9?

15. Who was Attorney-General in four successive Fianna Fail administrations, 1959–69?

Answers on page 102

1. Who was the only lady member of the Limerick Hell-Fire Club?

2. Which Limerick-born artist exhibited annually at the Royal Hibernian Academy from 1914 to 1975?

3. Where did St Finbarr die in A.D. 630?

4. In which Cork church can Hogan's 'Dead Christ' be seen?

5. Where can Cork City's only memorial to Daniel O'Connell be seen?

6. Which Clonmel-born writer was author of the major historical works *Ireland Under the Tudors* (1885–90) and *Ireland Under the Stuarts* (1909)?

7. Which Carrick-on-Suir inventor with his invention of the Royal Kent Bugle was the first to give a complete scale to brass instruments of the trumpet family?

8. Who granted Waterford its first charter after the Norman occupation?

9. Which Donegal man was conferred with the Freedom of the City of Waterford on 6 February 1877?

10. Which scholar was born at Dunaha, near Carrigaholt, Co. Clare, in 1796?

11. What does the rose motif on the arms of Co. Clare signify?

12. Where in 1645 did the Papal legate Rinucinni land?

13. Who translated O'Criomhthain's *An tOileanach* into English?

14. Where is the Clare Heritage Centre located?

Answers on page 102

1. Name the first Irish historical play staged in an Irish theatre.

2. Who in 1662 opened the Smock Alley Theatre in Dublin?

3. Which famous actress was said to have been 'discovered' selling apples at a theatre door by Madame Violante, a famous French tight-rope walker?

4. Which Dublin-born actor suffered considerable financial losses on his £22,000 investment in the Crow Street Theatre (1754–9)?

5. What was the real name of the actor Charles Macklin?

6. Who wrote to Disraeli demanding 'in the name of the Irish nation and the author of *The Shaughraun*, the release of the Fenian prisoners sentenced to death for the blowing-up of Clerkenwell prison'?

7. Which famous Irish playwright who died in 1964 once played the role of Fr Dolan in *The Shaughraun*?

8. Where did the historic meeting between W. B. Yeats, Edward Martyn and Lady Gregory, which gave rise to the Abbey Theatre, take place?

9. What was the family name of Lady Gregory?

10. How did Miss Annie Horniman come to endow the Abbey Theatre?

11. Why did Miss Horniman sever her connection with the Abbey in 1910?

12. In which US city in 1911 was the entire Abbey cast of *The Playboy of the Western World* arrested on a charge of presenting an immoral or indecent play?

Answers on page 103

1. Whose autobiography appeared in 1915 as *Mo Sgeal Fein*?

2. Whose 1938 autobiography was *Servant of the Queen*?

3. Whose prison experiences appeared in 1922 as *Glimpses of a Prison Felon's Life*?

4. *My Life in Two Hemispheres* (1898) is the autobiography of which famous nationalist?

5. Who was the author of the autobiographical *The Old Woman Remembers* recited by Sarah Allgood at the Abbey Theatre on 31 December 1923?

6. Name Christy Brown's 1970 autobiography.

7. *Allegiance* (1950) was the autobiography of which Wexford-born journalist, diplomat and Director of Broadcasting, Radio Eireann, 1947–8?

8. *My Fight for Irish Freedom* (1924) is the autobiography of which republican?

9. *Twice Around the Black Church* (1962) is the autobiography of which poet, playwright and novelist?

10. What is the title of sculptor Seamus Murphy's 1950 autobiography?

11. The opening of whose autobiography includes the words '. . . with one foot in the grave and another on its edge, I have experienced much ease . . .'?

12. Whose reminiscences of events leading up to the signing of the Anglo-Irish Treaty appeared in 1953 as *The Four Glorious Years*?

13. Whose autobiography was *An Only Child*?

14. *The Celtic Twilight* (1893) is an early volume of reminiscence and folklore. Name the author.

Answers on page 103

1. Who edited *Annals of the Kingdom of Ireland by the Four Masters* (1848–51)?

2. Who wrote *Phases of Irish History* (1937)?

3. Name the author of *Antiquities of the Irish Countryside* (1942).

4. Who wrote *Early Christian Art in Ireland* (1887)?

5. Who wrote *The United Irishmen Their Lives and Times* (1858–60)?

6. Name the author of *The Irish Tradition* (1947).

7. Who wrote *Early Irish Literature* (1948)?

8. Who in 1886 translated and edited *Cormac's Glossary*?

9. Name the husband and wife team responsible for *Early Christian Ireland*.

10. Who was the author of *Irish Life in the Seventeenth Century* (1939)?

11. Who in 1867 dedicated *The Story of Ireland* to 'My young fellow-countrymen at home and in exile . . .'?

12. Whose *A Dictionary of Irish Biography* appeared in 1978?

13. Whose magnum opus was *Bibliography of Irish Philology and Manuscript Literature, Publications, 1913–41* (1942)?

14. *The English in Ireland in the Eighteenth Century* (1872–4) is the work of which historian?

15. Who wrote *Dublin Under the Georges* (1956)?

Answers on page 104

1. Who replaced Thomas Davis as chief writer on the *Nation* (1845)?

2. Of whom did Charles Gavan Duffy say that 'he began with millions and reduced them to a score or a dozen'?

3. What Act, to deal with possible rebellion, was enacted in April 1848?

4. Who was the clerical supporter in Co. Tipperary who deserted Smith O'Brien prior to the rising in July 1848?

5. Who, though tried before a 'packed jury' in May 1848, was acquitted?

6. Who successfully defended Thomas Francis Meagher on charges of sedition in May 1845?

7. Which Pope issued a rescript on 5 February 1848 forbidding clerical involvement in politics?

8. Who was the Young Ireland Mayor of Kilkenny arrested on 29 July 1848?

9. Who arrived from Liverpool to aid William Smith O'Brien at Ballingarry in 1848?

10. Who commanded the police at Ballingarry on 30 July 1848?

11. Who was the Monaghan-born journalist who escaped to the USA while on bail in May 1848?

12. With what English organisation did Irish Confederates show solidarity in 1848?

13. Which Louth journalist returned from the USA to aid Daniel O'Connell and then joined Young Ireland?

14. Why were bonfires lit on 10–11 March 1848?

Answers on page 104

1. Who was PM on the outbreak of famine in 1845?

2. Who was Lord Lieutenant of Ireland on the outbreak of famine in 1845?

3. Who was Lord Lieutenant of Ireland from July 1846 until his death on 16 May 1847?

4. Who were the two persons who constituted the Scientific Commission appointed by Sir Robert Peel?

5. What was the value of the Indian corn (maize) purchased in the US by Sir Robert Peel?

6. Where in Co. Galway did Mrs Gerrard evict three hundred tenants on 13 March 1846?

7. Who was the 'Commissioner' of the London *Times* who gave an account of Ireland on the eve of the Famine (1845)?

8. Who was Whig Chancellor of the Exchequer from December 1846?

9. Who succeeded Sir Robert Peel as PM in June 1846?

10. How much money did Queen Victoria personally contribute to famine relief in Ireland?

11. Which distinguished soldier served as Chairman of the Relief Commission in 1847?

12. Where did Queen Victoria and Prince Albert land for their Irish visit of 1849?

13. Who, during the Famine, called on the Irish '. . . to unmuzzle the wolf dog'?

14. Who was Lord Mayor of Dublin during the royal visit in 1849?

15. Who was Under-Secretary during the Famine, 1845–9?

Answers on page 105

1. Who erected a huge hanging-garden at the rear of his Main Street, Limerick premises?

2. Who designed Waterford's Chamber of Commerce, City Hall and the city's two cathedrals?

3. Name the sculptor responsible for the Padraic O' Conaire statue in Eyre Square, Galway.

4. The Butlers of Kilkenny were paid £216,000 in 1811 for the loss of which privilege?

5. What Co. Louth town has a memorial to rescuers who perished on 9 April 1858 while attempting to save the crew of the *Mary Stoddard*?

6. Where is 'Main Guard'?

7. Who designed Sligo's 'Metal Man'?

8. Only one of Wexford's fortified gates remains. How many were there originally?

9. In what town does a brace of cannon commemorate Irishmen who fell in the Crimea and in the Indian Mutiny?

10. What is Longford's full and ancient name, commemorating a ruling family who built a castle and a Dominican Friary in the town, c. 1400?

11. What town's museum houses the fourteenth-century Cross of Clogher?

12. In what jail did Ireland's last hangwoman 'Lady Betty' ply her trade?

13. In what town are the ruins of the largest Anglo-Norman castle erected in Ireland?

Answers on page 105

1. What famous Dublin theatre closed down in June 1787?

2. What riotous event was held for the last time on 21–26 August 1854?

3. Who was the last Lord Lieutenant of Ireland?

4. Who was the last Governor-General of the Free State?

5. Where was the last major confrontation in the 'Tithe War' (1834)?

6. Who was the last Law Adviser to the British Government in Ireland?

7. Which Irishman was last Secretary-General of the League of Nations (1940–46)?

8. Who was the last of the 1921 Treaty signatories to die?

9. Who was the last Chief Secretary of Ireland?

10. For what was the Omagh-Fintona rail line notable?

11. Who was the last High King of Ireland?

12. Who was the last commander to surrender in Easter 1916?

13. Who was the last signatory to the Easter Proclamation?

14. Who was the last man executed for involvement in the 1916 Rising?

15. Who painted *The Last In*, a rural school scene?

Answers on page 106

Answers

The First Set (*page 1*)

1. Ptolemy of Alexander; the map indicated seven rivers and showed five towns.
2. *Saoirse* ('Freedom') skippered by Conor O'Brien (1880–1952).
3. Mellifont Abbey, Co. Louth, built by the Cistercians c. 1157.
4. Cearbhall O'Dalaigh (1911–78) in 1972.
5. Sligo, 1919; first general use was in local government elections, January 1920.
6. *Sunday Freeman's Journal* (1817).
7. Denis Ireland (1894–1974).
8. Sean MacBride (the Lawless internment case).
9. Fahan, Co. Donegal.
10. Limerick (18 December 1179, pre-dating London by a decade).
11. The Black Death (Bubonic Plague).
12. First ascent by balloon in Ireland, from Ranelagh Gardens to North Strand, Dublin.
13. Ollamh Fodhla.
14. Nial III.

The Northern Province (*page 2*)

1. J. R. Fisher.
2. Ulster Folk Museum.
3. Ulster Unionist Council.
4. Walter Long, First Viscount Long of Wraxall, (1854–1924).
5. Prohibition of alcoholic drink (founded in 1929 by Rev. A. Wylie Blue).
6. Frederick Augustus Hervey, Fourth Earl of Bristol; Bishop of Derry (1768–1803).
7. Irish Loyal and Patriotic Union (ILPU).
8. Lt Gen. Erskine Crum (suffered a heart attack and died on 17 March).

9. Merchant seaman.
10. John Miller Andrews (1871–1956).
11. Geoffrey Bing.
12. Eddie McAteer (1914–86).
13. Walter Long.
14. Humphrey Atkins.
15. Loyalist Association of Workers (LAW).

Words of Wisdom (*page 3*)

1. Charles Stewart Parnell.
2. Senator W. B. Yeats.
3. Rev. Ian Paisley.
4. Garrett Mor FitzGerald, Eighth Earl of Kildare (d. 1513).
5. General Eoin O'Duffy (1892–1944).
6. '. . . but no man has the right to fix the boundary of the march of a nation' (quoted on the Parnell Monument in Dublin).
7. Sir Boyle Roche (1743–1807), originator of the Irish 'bull'.
8. Dr Noel Browne.
9. Kevin O'Higgins (1892–1927).
10. Thomas Babington Macauley (1800–1859).

Politics (I) (*page 4*)

1. John Dillon (1851–1927).
2. Neil T. Blaney.
3. Brendan Corish.
4. Sean Moylan (1888–1957).
5. T. P. O'Connor (1848–1929).
6. Thomas Derrig (1897–1956).
7. Gerald Boland (1885–1973).
8. William O'Brien (1852–1928).

9. Sean T. O'Kelly (1882–1966).
10. Clann Eireann.
11. John Martin (1812–75).
12. Clann na Talmhan.
13. Clann na Poblachta.
14. Erskine Childers (1931–6).
15. 1922.

Founding Fathers (I) (*page 5*)

1. Dungannon Clubs.
2. Arthur Griffith (1871–1922).
3. Paddy 'The Cope' Gallagher (1873–1964).
4. Frederick Lucas (1812–55).
5. The GAA.
6. Ballintubber Abbey, Co. Mayo.
7. Dr Roy Johnston.
8. Royal Society of Antiquaries of Ireland (RSAI).
9. Blarney, Co. Cork.
10. Catholic Boy Scouts of Ireland.
11. Dean Richard O'Brien of Limerick.
12. Campaign for Social Justice.
13. United Irish League.
14. Dunmanway, Co. Cork.
15. Richard Boyle, Earl of Cork.

Fenians (*page 6*)

1. John O'Mahony (1816–77).
2. Michael Doheny (1805–63).
3. Ricard O'Sullivan Burke (1838–1922).
4. Gustave Paul Cluseret (1823–1900).
5. Col Thomas J. Kelly (1833–1908).
6. T. D. Sullivan (1827–1914).
7. Inspector John Mallon.

8. Fr Patrick Lavelle (1825–86).
9. Thomas F. Burke.
10. John J. Corydon.
11. Fr Patrick Lavelle.
12. Phoenix Park Murders (executed between 14 May and 9 June 1883).
13. Jeremiah O'Donovan (Rossa) (1831–1915).
14. John Devoy (1842–1928) (to gain military experience to use when fighting in Ireland).
15. Bishop David Moriarty of Kerry (1867).

'Beautiful City' (*page 7*)

1. Richard Wine (previous office-holders were known as 'provosts').
2. St Finbarr's South (1766).
3. 1172.
4. For services against the Earl of Desmond.
5. 1750.
6. Daniel O'Connell.
7. Opening of Cork Park Racecourse (closed May 1916).
8. Daniel J. Hegarty (later knighted).
9. Sir Thomas Deane (a Corkman), assisted by Benjamin Woodward.
10. 1920: Thomas MacCurtain (murdered by Crown forces, 20 March); Terence MacSwiney (died on hunger strike, Brixton Prison, 24 October); Donal O'Callaghan (re-elected 1921, 1922 and 1923).
11. June 1954.
12. Opera House destroyed by fire (new Opera House opened officially on 31 October 1965).
13. 16 October 1961.
14. 1985.
15. 1883 (the Cork International Exhibition was held 1902–3).

Miscellany (I) (*page 8*)

1. Herman Goertz.
2. Eoin MacNeill's (1867–1945).
3. *Muirchu* (formerly the *Helga* which had shelled central Dublin in Easter 1916).
4. Dan Breen (in April).
5. Prof. E. T. Walton (with Sir John Cockcroft), for work in the field of atomic nuclei.
6. Frank Aiken (1898–1983).
7. Joseph Gillis Biggar (1828–90).
8. Captain Francis O'Neill (1849–1936).
9. Thomas Ashe.
10. Irish Citizen Army.
11. Erskine Childers.
12. Francis Pym.
13. Joseph Timothy Haydn.
14. Co. Cavan (b. Cootehill, 28 July 1895).

A Set of Names (*page 9*)

1. Aherne (O'hEachthighearna: 'each' = steed; 'tigher-ana' = lord).
2. MacAleese (Mac Giolla Iosa).
3. The Coopers.
4. The O'Shaughnessys.
5. The de Veres.
6. The O'Mahonys.
7. A name derived from a place name (examples are few in Irish nomenclature — Craughwell, Co. Galway, is an exception).
8. Munster.
9. Limerick.
10. The MacCarthys (Mac Carthaigh: 'carthach' = loving).
11. Scotland.
12. Tipperary.

13. Burke.
14. O'Sullivan.
15. The O'Conor Don.

Land for the People (*page 10*)

1. A. H. Smith-Barry, Lord Barrymore (1843–1925).
2. Bodyke evictions, Co. Clare.
3. Peep O' Day Boys.
4. Graiguenamanagh.
5. Fr Eugene Sheehy (1841–1917; arrested on 20 May 1881).
6. Lord Mountmorres.
7. Timothy Harrington (1851–1910).
8. James Fintan Lalor (b. 1807).
9. Woodford, Co. Galway when Thomas Saunders resisted attempts at eviction.
10. Fr Patrick Lavelle (1825–86).
11. Canon James McFadden (1842–1917).
12. James Daly (1836–1910).
13. Derryveagh, Co. Donegal.
14. Fr Matthew Ryan (1844–1937).

United Irishmen (*page 11*)

1. *The Northern Star*.
2. General Lake's.
3. Rev. William Jackson.
4. Lord Cornwallis.
5. Rutland Island, Co. Donegal.
6. General Sir Ralph Abercrombie.
7. General Lake.
8. Joseph Stock (1740–1813).
9. Betsy Grey.
10. Beauchamp Bagenal Harvey.
11. John Moore.
12. Richard Robert Madden.

13. Thomas Reynolds (betrayed the Leinster Directory).
14. Leonard MacNally.

Religion (I) (*page 12*)

1. Rev. Edward Nangle.
2. Monsignor Ignazio Persico.
3. Gougane Barra, Co. Cork.
4. 'Church of God' or 'Walkerites'.
5. Dr Thomas Hussey.
6. Alfred O'Rahilly (1884–1969).
7. Yugoslavia.
8. Adare, Co. Limerick (suppressed 1535).
9. Francis McKenna (b. Gartan, Co. Donegal, 1680).
10. Presbyterian Church.
11. Society of Jesus (Jesuits).
12. Cornelius O'Devaney.
13. Carmelites.
14. Pope Celestine.
15. Dermot O'Hurley.

'The Sea, Oh! The Sea' (*page 13*)

1. John Paul Jones.
2. *Princess Victoria*.
3. *The Chotah* or *The Kelpie*.
4. Coastal and Marine Service (Naval Service since 1947).
5. *Hibernia*.
6. *Catalpa*.
7. William Ritchie (a Scotsman).
8. *Laurentic* (gold recovered within seven years).
9. *Sirius* (first ship to cross the Atlantic solely under steam in 1838).
10. *Rob Roy* (13–14 June 1818).
11. *Aud*.
12. John Mitchel (being transported to Van Dieman's Land [Tasmania]).

13. *Kowloon Bridge*.
14. Foodships from England for Dublin workers involved in the Lock-Out of 1913.
15. *Claudia*.

By Any Other Name (I) (*page 14*)

1. Richard de Clare ('Strongbow'; d. 1176).
2. John Scott, Earl of Clonmell (1739–98).
3. Iarla an tSugain ('The Sugan or Straw-Rope Earl'; d. 1608).
4. Rex Ingram (1893–1950), Hollywood film director.
5. Canon James McFadden (1842–1917).
6. Declaratory Act (1720).
7. *Muirchu*.
8. Leo Rowsome (1900–1970).
9. 'Zozimus'.
10. F. J. McCormick (1889–1947); theatre and film actor.
11. 'Buck' Mulligan.
12. James Clarence Mangan (1803–49).
13. Seamus O'Sullivan (1879–1958).
14. Sir Richard Church (1784–1873).
15. Timothy Buckley (1863–1945).

Founding Fathers (II) (*page 15*)

1. Irish Creamery Milk Suppliers Association (ICMSA).
2. Kildare Street Club.
3. Sir Horace Plunkett (1854–1932).
4. An Tur Gloine (The Glass Tower).
5. Rev. Dr Cornelius Lucey.
6. Fr James O'Flynn (1881–1962).
7. Delia Larkin.
8. White Quakers.
9. Fr Thomas Finlay or Fr Matthew Russell.
10. Brunswick (Constitutional) Club.
11. Maria Duce.

12. 'Hell-Fire Club'.
13. Rev. Stephen James Brown.
14. Mary MacSwiney (c. 1872–1942).
15. Royal Irish Academy of Music.

Miscellany (II) (*page 16*)

1. Bessborough Commission.
2. Kilbrogan, Bandon, Co. Cork (now secularised).
3. *The Protestant Telegraph*.
4. Sir George Carew.
5. Major-General Sir Hubert Gough.
6. Sir John Andrew Stevenson.
7. The Hunt Commission.
8. Charles Bianconi (1785–1875).
9. Both were sunk during World War 2.
10. Marquess of Aberdeen (1896; 1905–15).
11. As an oculist.
12. St Columba's College, Rathfarnham, Dublin.
13. James J. McElligott (1893–1974).
14. Lord Leitrim.
15. Horse-drawn tram-cars.

Newspapers (*page 17*)

1. *The Irish People*.
2. Percy French (1854–1920).
3. Isaac Butt (1813–79).
4. *The Irish Homestead*.
5. R. M. Smyllie.
6. Patrick Ford's *Irish World*.
7. Frank Gallagher ('David Hogan') (1898–1962).
8. John O'Leary (1830–1907).
9. Matthew Bodkin.
10. Patrick Campbell.
11. John Devoy (1842–1928).
12. *Connaught Telegraph*.

13. *Limerick Chronicle* (founded in 1766 by John Ferrar).
14. Patrick Pearse.
15. Alice Milligan (1865–1953).

Ancient Ireland (*page 18*)

1. The Hill of Uisneach.
2. A small harp, tuned to blend with the larger harp.
3. *The Annals of Inishfallen*.
4. The Griannan of Aileach.
5. A female slave used as barter; at one stage she was equal to six heifers.
6. Books (a custom also common in the East).
7. The *Dinnseanchus*.
8. *The Book of Armagh* (contents include the Confession of St Patrick and a copy of the New Testament).
9. Women were summarily burned. Men had to pay the 'enechlan' or honour-price — legally-defined amount due to the injured party for loss of honour.
10. 'Men of Art', the learned class: poets, musicians and the skilled craftsmen.
11. The personal slave of a chief.
12. Cuchulainn's chariot horse.
13. Heavily-salted, preserved butter, bitter to the taste (usually buried in bogs for preservation and remained edible over long periods).
14. One-tenth of the cost of the item(s).
15. Leprechauns.

Wars of the Gael (*page 19*)

1. Dysert O'Dea, Co. Clare.
2. Battle of the Yellow Ford (14 August 1598). The 'brave Marshal' is Sir Henry Bagenal who was killed in action and the 'Avon-Duff' is the Blackwater.
3. Lieut General Ginkel.
4. The Boyne (1 July 1690).

5. Rory O'Connor at the Battle of Dublin, 1171.
6. James Fitzmaurice (FitzGerald).
7. The Battle of Knockdoe, Co. Galway.
8. Clontibret (27 May 1595).
9. Farsetmore, Co. Donegal.
10. Kinsale (1601).
11. Don Diego de Brochero (Don Juan del Aguila was *land* commander).
12. Dungan's Hill, near Trim, Co. Meath.
13. Sir Conyers Clifford.
14. Gabhra: the Fianna were routed by the High King Cairbre of the Liffey.

Miscellany (III) (*page 20*)

1. Thomas Moore (stanza by Henry Lutrell).
2. Reported apparition at Knock.
3. Muintir na Tire.
4. Marion Price.
5. Ceramic miniatures.
6. Michael Angelo Hayes (1820–77).
7. W. B. Yeats (1865–1939).
8. Amergin (Aimirgin).
9. Thomas Moore (the 'duel' was a farcical affair — both sets of seconds had removed the respective bullets).
10. Francis MacManus (1909–65).
11. Ballad-singer Delia Murphy.

Set for a Genius (*page 21*)

1. The Botanic Gardens, Dublin.
2. Crookhaven, Co. Cork.
3. Turlough O'Connor, King of Connaught.
4. Lord Kingsborough.
5. Sir William Petty.
6. Sir Edward Sabine (1788–1883).
7. John Alen.

8. St Stephen's.
9. John Hogan.
10. The stair-carpet.
11. John Dillon, MP.
12. Michael Hayes (1889–1976).
13. Pottery.
14. Micheal Mac Liammoir.
15. Gerald, Earl of Desmond (at Glenageenty, near Tralee, Co. Kerry).

Religion II (*page 22*)

1. Rev. Henry Montgomery.
2. Terence Albert O'Brien.
3. Society of Jesus (Jesuits).
4. Dr James McCann.
5. Catholic Archbishopric of Dublin.
6. Laurence O'Toole.
7. Fr Michael O'Hickey.
8. Quin, Co. Clare.
9. Franciscans.
10. Holy Cross, Co. Tipperary.
11. Thurles, Co. Tipperary.
12. James Warren Doyle ('JKL').
13. Portumna, Co. Galway.
14. Palladius.
15. Clonfert.

Mna na hEireann (Women of Ireland) (*page 23*)

1. Maire ni Scolai, traditional singer.
2. Nora Owen.
3. Margaret Anne Cusack (1832–99).
4. Peggy Dell.
5. Louie Bennett (1870–1956), elected at the 1932 Cork Conference.
6. Castlebar, Co. Mayo.

7. Sarah Curran.
8. Catherine Hayes (1825–61).
9. Margaret Cousins (*nee* Gillespie, 1878–1954).
10. Gretta Bowen (Mrs Matthew Campbell, mother of artists Arthur and George).
11. Leslie, Bean de Barra (1893–1984).
12. Anna Johnston ('Ethna Carbery'; 1866–1911).
13. Unionist Party of Northern Ireland (she succeeded Brian Faulkner who resigned in 1976).

Holy Ireland (*page 24*)

1. St Finnian.
2. Tullylease, Co. Cork.
3. St Kevin of Glendalough.
4. St Ciaran (feast-day on 5 March).
5. St Jarlath.
6. St Fursey (feast-day on 16 January).
7. St Gobnait (feast-day on 11 February).
8. St Ita or Ide who founded a nunnery at Killeedy (Church of Ide).
9. St Macartan (feast-day on 24 March).
10. St Ruadhan of Lorrha (feast-day on 15 April).
11. The Flannan Islands (after St Flannan of Killaloe, Co. Clare).

Men of Letters (*page 25*)

1. Arthur William Conway (President, 1940–47).
2. Sir Richard John Griffith (1784–1878).
3. Astronomy.
4. Prof. George O'Brien (1892–1973).
5. Fr Michael O'Flanagan (1876–1942).
6. Irish history.
7. Sylvester O'Halloran (1728–1807).
8. Osborn Bergin (1873–1950).
9. Arland Ussher (1899–1980).

10. P. W. Joyce (1827–1914).
11. William Thompson (c. 1785–1833).
12. Luke Wadding (1588–1657).
13. *Giraldus Cambrensis* (Gerald the Welshman).
14. John O'Donovan (1809–61).

Miscellany (IV) (*page 26*)

1. Darrell Figgis (1882–1925).
2. James Dillon (John Blake Dillon was his grandfather).
3. Rev. George Walker (1618–90; killed at Battle of the Boyne).
4. Col Thomas Blood (1618–80).
5. Conciliation Hall.
6. Catholic Emancipation.
7. Twenty-second of June 1921 when George V opened the Parliament of Northern Ireland.
8. *Glenanaar* by Canon P. A. Sheehan (1852–1913).
9. Capt. W. H. O'Shea.
10. *The Irish Felon*.
11. Eoin MacNeill (1867–1945).
12. General Sir Nevil Macready (1862–1945).
13. Fr John Henry Newman (later Cardinal).
14. Columbanus (c. 543–615).
15. Manhattan.

West Quest (*page 27*)

1. Fourteen.
2. Richard Joyce.
3. Francis A. Fahy (1854–1935).
4. Robert Lloyd Praeger in *The Way That I Went*.
5. Robert O'Hara Burke (1820–61).
6. Mairtin O'Cadhain (1906–70); *Cre na Cille* (1949).
7. James Hardiman (c.1790–1855).
8. G. A. Hayes–McCoy.
9. Mary Letitia Martin (1815–50).

10. Queen Anne.
11. Its quincentennial.
12. At the Collegiate Church of St Nicholas, Galway.
13. Worn as a betrothal-token, the heart inclines towards the nail of the finger; on marriage the ring is reversed, with the crown nearest the fingernail.

A Question of Design (*page 28*)

1. 'The Metal Man', Tramore, Co. Waterford.
2. Francis Johnston (1760–1829).
3. Sir Thomas Deane (1828–99; also designed National Museum).
4. Thomas Andrews of Harland and Wolff (went down with ship).
5. Harry Clarke's (1889–1931).
6. Niall Montgomery.
7. Richard Cassells (completed by his partner John Ensor).
8. Richard Cassells (in collaboration with Francis Bindon).
9. Sir William Chambers.
10. Augustus Saint-Gaudens.
11. Thomas Burgh, in 1712.
12. Edward Parke in 1806 (extended, in 1826, by William Murray).
13. Matthew Bridge.
14. Barry Byrne.
15. Messrs Jones and Kelly, Dublin.

The Sixties (*page 29*)

1. Cyril Cusack.
2. 1967 (February).
3. Those of John Millington Synge.
4. Kilkenny Castle (handed over to the Castle Restoration Committee by the Marquess of Ormond).

5. Jayne Mansfield (she died three weeks later in a car accident).
6. Sir Alfred Chester Beatty (b. 1875).
7. 1968 (20 September).
8. (3 November) 1969.
9. 1964.
10. To make way for car showrooms.
11. 1966.
12. 1969 (9 December).
13. A. J. F. (Tony) O'Reilly.
14. Retirement of the last dray-horse owned by the company in Dublin.

The Seventies (*page 30*)

1. Amsterdam.
2. Jack B. Yeats.
3. 1972 (1 September).
4. Dmitri Shostakovich.
5. Ashford Castle, Cong, Co. Mayo.
6. Eddie Gallagher and Dr Rose Dugdale.
7. 1979 (31 May).
8. Eamon de Valera and John A. Costello.
9. They were taken over by Quinnsworth.
10. Twenty-eighth of November 1977.
11. Mervyn Taylor.
12. Department of Economic Planning.
13. Delia Murphy.
14. Timahoe, Co. Kildare.

The Eighties (*page 31*)

1. Major six-week Festival of Irish Arts and Culture which opened in London on 1 February 1980.
2. Britain (Buck's Fizz with 'Makin' Your Mind Up').
3. The Workers' Party.
4. Bob Dylan.

5. Irish Shipping Ltd.
6. Lord Fitt of Bell's Hill.
7. 'Durty Nelly's', (Bunratty).
8. 1982 (23 April).
9. St Kieran's, Kilkenny (first diocesan college in Ireland, following Catholic Relief Act 1782).
10. Ireland's first woman soldiers, at the Curragh Camp.
11. Mr Justice Declan Costello.
12. Miriam Hederman O'Brien.
13. Michael Killeen.
14. 1981 (10 September).
15. John Robb (later made a Senator).

Founding Fathers (III) (*page 32*)

1. Sean (Dublin Bay) Loftus.
2. T. W. Russell.
3. Patrick Belton.
4. Protestant Home Rule Association.
5. Irish National Federation.
6. Isaac Butt.
7. *The Bell*.
8. Society of Friends or Quakers.
9. The College of Physicians.
10. James Connolly (1896).
11. Fr Leo Close.
12. Dublin Society (or Royal Dublin Society as it became in 1731).
13. R. Dudley Edwards and T. W. Moody (1938).
14. National Centre (with James Dillon).
15. Dr Bartholomew Mosse (1745).

By Any Other Name II (*page 33*)

1. Seanascal.
2. 'Adventurers' Act' (1642).
3. Sean Caomhanach (Sean Kavanagh).

4. St Lawrence.
5. St Columcille.
6. Padraig O' Siochfhradha (1883–1964).
7. Peig Sayers.
8. 'Black Tom'.
9. *Leabhar Gabhala*.
10. Caulfield.
11. Francis Higgins (1746–1802).
12. Theobald Wolfe Tone.
13. 'Charter Schools'.
14. Lord Offaly.
15. 'Hawarden Kite'.

Miscellany (V) (*page 34*)

1. Lambert Simnel.
2. George Mulvany (1809–69).
3. Timothy Harrington (1851–1910).
4. Clare (1880).
5. Connolly (formerly Amiens Street Station).
6. The Ardagh Hoard (Ardagh Chalice and other items).
7. 1951.
8. Sir Horace Plunkett (1854–1932).
9. Peter O'Brien (1842–1914).
10. The Augustinian Canons.
11. Milesmen.
12. Owen Roe O'Neill.
13. Belleek Pottery.
14. Anne Devlin (housekeeper to Robert Emmet).

History in Verse (*page 35*)

1. 'The Fool' (Patrick Pearse).
2. Francis Ledwidge ('Lament for the Poets, 1916').
3. James Connell (c. 1850–1929).
4. That of Ethna Carbery (1866–1911).
5. 'The Siege of Limerick', poem by R. D. Joyce.

6. Douglas Hyde (1860–1949).
7. 'The Burial of King Cormac' (Sir Samuel Ferguson).
8. P. J. McCall (1861–1919).
9. Thomas Davis (1814–45).
10. 'The Man From God Knows Where' (Thomas Russell, United Irishman).
11. Thomas D'Arcy McGee (1825–68).
12. 'A Munster War Song'.
13. Lady Wilde (1826–96).
14. William Allingham (1824–89).
15. House painter.

The Press in Ireland (*page 36*)

1. T. D. Sullivan (author of *God Save Ireland*).
2. GAA.
3. *Irish World*.
4. John Devoy.
5. *The United Irishman*.
6. *The Nation* (1842).
7. *Southern Star*.
8. *The Pilot*.
9. Richard Pigott.
10. Arthur Griffith.
11. George Russell ('AE').
12. *An Claideamh Soluis* ('Sword of Light'), Gaelic League journal.
13. William O'Brien.
14. *The Leader*.
15. *Belfast Newsletter*.

Battles (*page 37*)

1. Heber MacMahon.
2. Earl of Ormond.
3. Dunboy Castle, Berehaven, Co. Cork.
4. Sir Peter Carew.

5. Brian Boru.
6. Henry Ireton.
7. Near Baltinglass, Co. Wicklow.
8. John de Bermingham.
9. Burkes of Castleconnell, Co. Limerick.
10. St Colmcille.
11. Edmund Magauran.
12. Cormac Mac Cuilleanain of Munster.
13. Fiach Mac Hugh O'Byrne.
14. Murrough O'Brien, Lord Inchiquin's troops.
15. Mahon MacKennedy (brother of Brian Boru).

Northern Ireland (*page 38*)

1. Brian Faulkner.
2. Duke of Abercorn.
3. Terence O'Neill.
4. T. G. McAllister.
5. Brian Faulkner.
6. Hugh de Fellenberg Montgomery.
7. George B. Newe (appointed by Brian Faulkner).
8. Sir John Oliver Wright.
9. Ulster Volunteer Force (UVF).
10. Four (Antrim, Armagh, Down and Londonderry).
11. Sir Leslie Scarman.
12. Harry Midgely.
13. Progressive Unionist Party.
14. John Hanna Robb.
15. Burntollet Bridge.

Land of Our Birth (*page 39*)

1. Roscommon (b. Castlerea, 1815).
2. Cork.
3. Waterford.
4. Dysart Castle, Co. Kilkenny.
5. Theobald Wolfe Tone.

6. St Brigid.
7. Dublin.
8. Bantry, Co. Cork.
9. Foxford, Co. Mayo.
10. Meath (born near Nobber, c. 1670).
11. Kilkenny.
12. Dublin.
13. Tyrone (b. Cookstown, 10 April 1865).
14. London.
15. Lucan, Co. Dublin.

Poets and Poetry (*page 40*)

1. Torna.
2. A monk's pet cat.
3. Eochadh O'Hussey.
4. Turlough Carolan.
5. Aindreas Mac Craith (the 'Mangaire Sugach' or 'Merry Pedlar').
6. 'The Convict of Clonmel'.
7. 'The Midnight Court' (Brian Merriman).
8. Anthony Raftery.
9. Jonathan Swift (1667–1745).
10. 'A bold peasantry'.
11. John O'Keeffe (1747–1833).
12. Owen Roe O'Sullivan (1748–84).
13. Patrick O'Kelly (Lady Doneraile presented him with a new watch and he recanted his curse in 'Blessings of Doneraile').
14. William Drennan (1754–1820).

Politics (II) (*page 41*)

1. Prof. Timothy Smiddy.
2. William Shaw.
3. Dr James Ryan.
4. Liam Cosgrave.

5. One hundred and twenty eight.
6. Patrick J. Ruttledge.
7. William Vesey Fitzgerald.
8. United Ireland Party.
9. Kieran Doherty.
10. William Norton.
11. Dr Garret FitzGerald.
12. Count Plunkett.
13. General Eoin O'Duffy (1892–1944).
14. National Council.
15. Liam Cosgrave.

Founding Fathers (IV) (*page 42*)

1. Siamsa Tíre.
2. John Scott Vandaleur.
3. Property Defence Association.
4. William Sharman Crawford (1781–1861).
5. Tenant (Right) League.
6. The Pike.
7. Arthur Griffith and William Rooney.
8. That of Chief Secretary E. G. Stanley (later Lord Derby) (1799–1869).
9. Thomas H. ('Tod') Sloan (1870–1941).
10. David Thornley.
11. Daniel O'Connell.
12. The first Tenants' Protection Society.
13. William Martin Murphy (1844–1919).
14. Charlestown, Co. Mayo.
15. T. M. Healy (1855–1931).

The Irish in England (*page 43*)

1. Nahum Tate (1652–1715); succeeded Shadwell in 1692.
2. George Canning.
3. Thomas Doggett ('Doggett's Coat and Badge').
4. Capt. Francis Fowke (1823–65).

5. Dr Samuel Johnson (the publisher was Newbery).
6. Richard Creagh (a belief persists that he may have been poisoned).
7. Richard Lalor Sheil (the coin was not inscribed '*Fidei Defensatrix Dei Gratia*').
8. Tyrone (born in Caledon, 10 December 1891).
9. Master William Betty (as an eleven year-old his first London season grossed £17,500).
10. Shakespeare's life and works.
11. Arthur Wellesley, First Duke of Wellington (1769–1852).
12. Richard Doyle (d. 11 December 1883).

By Any Other Name (III) (*page 44*)

1. Daniel Maclise (1806–70).
2. Dr Donnelly, Bishop of Dromore.
3. Thomas Steele (1788–1848).
4. 'Speranza' (1826–96).
5. Hazel, Lady Lavery.
6. John T. Campion (b. 1814).
7. John Keegan Casey (1846–70).
8. Francis Davis (d. 1885).
9. William Kenealy (d. 1876).
10. Mary Eva Kelly (1826–1910); later Mrs Kevin Izod O'Doherty.
11. John O'Hagan (1822–90).
12. John Fitzgerald (1825–1910).
13. Edward Carson.
14. 'The Colleen Bawn'.
15. 'Mr Ellis'.

What Year (*page 45*)

1. 1946.
2. 1829 (the trial was a triumph for Daniel O'Connell).
3. 1839.

4. 1926 (5 September).
5. 1936 (Baldonnel – Bristol).
6. 1737.
7. 1928.
8. 1953.
9. 1915.
10. 1920 (1 November).
11. 1909 (Synge died on 24 March; ITGWU formed on 4 January).
12. 1941 (Joyce died on 13 January; Irish Shipping formed in March).
13. 1934.
14. 1845 (Davis died on 16 September; *Maritana* had its Drury Lane premiere on 15 November).

Where? (*page 46*)

1. Holles Street.
2. Cornwall.
3. Newry and Lough Neagh (1741).
4. Kanturk, Co. Cork.
5. Assembly Rooms, Cork.
6. Kilkea, Co. Kildare.
7. Charles Fort, Kinsale, Co. Cork.
8. Summerhill, Dublin.
9. Ightermurragh Castle, Co. Cork.
10. Cornwall (it was taken apart and re-built on its present site).
11. Asdee, Co. Kerry.
12. Woodenbridge, Co. Wicklow.
13. On the O'Connell Monument, O'Connell Street, Dublin.
14. Trinity College Dublin; they are red-brick residences built in the reign of Queen Anne.
15. Gartan, Co. Donegal (A.D. 521).

War of Independence (*page 47*)

1. White Cross.
2. Jeremiah Mee (1889–1953).
3. Sean Mac Eoin (1893–1973).
4. General Lucas (he 'escaped' some five weeks later).
5. Tom Barry (1897–1980).
6. General Richard Mulcahy (1886–1971).
7. Liam Lynch (1890–1973).
8. Medicine.
9. Mallow, Co. Cork (by units of Cork No. 2 (North) Brigade under Liam Lynch and Ernie O'Malley).
10. *On Another Man's Wound*.
11. Dan Breen and Sean Treacy.
12. Talbot Street.
13. First RIC Barracks in Ulster to be captured.
14. Tom Barry, at Kilmichael and Crossbarry.
15. Sixth of December.

Scientists and Inventors (*page 48*)

1. Terence Millin (1903–80); 'Millin's prostatectomy'.
2. Dr Nicholas Callan (1799–1864).
3. Woulfe's Bottle (twin-necked apparatus used in chemical laboratories).
4. Louis Brennan (1852–1932).
5. Thomas Grubb (1800–78).
6. Surgery ('Bennett's Fracture').
7. Performed first operation using anaesthetic in Ireland.
8. Allan Mullen (or Molines).
9. Robert Mallet (1810–81).
10. 'Kyanising' (a method of preserving wood).
11. Telescope built by the Third Earl of Rosse at Birr Castle (1845) (remained largest in the world for many years).
12. Sir Robert Kane (1809–90).
13. Lucien Ball (1876–1972).

14. William Thomson, First Baron Kelvin (1824–1907).
15. Thomas Andrews (1813–85).

Legends of the Gael (*page 49*)

1. Dianecht.
2. The sons of Tuireann.
3. The Formorians.
4. Lugh Lamhfada (Lugh of the Long Arm).
5. Naoise, son of Usnach.
6. She stabbed herself.
7. By asking him to measure the skin of a wild boar by treading; one of the bristles inflicted a mortal wound.
8. The Goban Saor.
9. The sword of Conor Mac Nessa.
10. Cliona.
11. Fand.
12. Ailill.
13. Cathbad.
14. Slaying Ulstermen!
15. The sword of Manannan Mac Lir; its every wound was fatal.

A Question of Dates (*page 50*)

1. The Gaelic League.
2. 1869.
3. The Connaught Rangers'.
4. 1839.
5. 1953.
6. Radio na Gaeltachta.
7. 1834.
8. The Land League.
9. Queen's University in Ireland (Queen's Colleges).
10. Wexford Opera Festival.
11. 1959.
12. The Limavady (Broighter) Gold Hoard.

13. (Saint) Oliver Plunkett.
14. The Salvation Army.
15. The Listowel-Ballybunion Lartigue Monorail.

Dust to Dust (*page 51*)

 1. James Barry (1741–1806).
 2. He choked on a salmon-bone.
 3. Robert Stewart, Viscount Castlereagh (1769–1822).
 4. Brompton Cemetery.
 5. The Bowl of Light and its surround, erected for 'An Tostal' on O'Connell Bridge.
 6. Bromham Churchyard, Bedfordshire.
 7. Kensal Green, London.
 8. Glasnevin, Dublin.
 9. Oliver Bond.
10. Edinburgh.
11. Stranorlar, Co. Donegal.
12. In the garden of his Ayot St Lawrence home.
13. Mount Jerome, Dublin.
14. Oscar Wilde.
15. Newry, Co. Down.

Pot-Pourri (*page 52*)

 1. Two.
 2. Sir Richard John Griffith (1784–1878).
 3. Archbishop Croke of Cashel (1824–1902).
 4. Cork Historical and Archaeological Society.
 5. Republican Labour Party.
 6. £10.
 7. 1954.
 8. The Yeats family.
 9. Denis Devlin (1908–59).
10. Dermot MacMurrough (Kavanagh).
11. Austin Clarke.
12. Saffron-coloured.

13. Emer (said to have been a gifted embroideress).
14. 'Boycott'.
15. Major-General Michael J. Costello (1904–86).

Can You Score 10? (*page 53*)

1. Embroidery (the workers stitched pre-stamped articles).
2. Engraving.
3. Brian Boru ('Emperor of the Irish').
4. St Malachy.
5. The Abbey Church at Mellifont, Co. Louth.
6. Limerick (it may have been the first such establishment in Europe).
7. 'Countrywear' (c. 1948).
8. Sir Samuel Ferguson (1810–86).
9. Roscrea.
10. Enniscorthy Castle, Co. Wexford.
11. After Cape Martella, Corsica where the British captured a tower of this type.
12. John Hughes (1865–1941).
13. The Local Government Board.
14. Henry Cromwell.

More 'Firsts' (*page 54*)

1. *Casadh an tSugain* ('The Twisting of the Rope') in 1901.
2. Cork City (1929).
3. Ford Model N (four-cylinder car displayed at the Irish Motor Show in 1907).
4. Michael Staines (February 1922).
5. Opposition to the Union.
6. Viscount Townshend.
7. 5p and 10p coins.
8. South Dublin Union.
9. Dublin Horse Show.
10. Hugh Boyle Kennedy (1879–1936).

11. 'Whiskey' (he died from over-indulgence in Leitrim).
12. As author of the first book printed in Ireland (*Aibidil Gaoidheilge & Caiticiosma* — 'Gaelic Alphabet & Catechism').
13. Historian Mary Teresa Hayden (1862–1942).
14. *The Irish Rose*.
15. Richard Pockrich (b. Co. Monaghan in 1759).

An Ancient 'What' (*page 55*)

1. Open-air cooking areas where the spoils of the chase were roasted.
2. Avenue leading to the fort of a king.
3. Originally it meant 'cattleway', and is defined in Cormac's *Glossary* as one in which 'two cows fit upon it, one lengthwise, the other sideways, their calves and yearlings with them'.
4. Ancient form of measure described as 'twelve times the full of a hen's egg'.
5. Argyll: 'Airthir-Gaedhil' (Eastern Gaels).
6. 'The Forty Years' Rest'.
7. Council which elected and advised the monarch and which was responsible for the rule of kingly succession.
8. A youth studying to be a bard.
9. Acceptance by the plaintiff as compensation of a different item than that originally stolen, injured, destroyed or promised.
10. 'Brat'.
11. The Cellarium (usually in the west range of the cloister).
12. Small closed spherical or pear-shaped bell sounded by a loose metal ball or pea.
13. Irish druids did not offer human sacrifice.
14. When he was seventeen or when he started to grow a beard.

15. The slaying of kin, regarded as the worst crime in the Irish calendar.

Legends of the Fianna (*page 56*)

1. Diarmuid (Dermot).
2. Caoilte Mac Ronain.
3. Conan (the epithet 'maol' meaning 'bald' was applied to him).
4. Oisin (she regained human form when pursued and captured by Fionn).
5. The Hill of Allen in Co. Kildare.
6. Giolla Deachair.
7. Cormac Mac Art.
8. O'Duibhne.
9. Fionn was his uncle.
10. Deimne.
11. In the Slieve Bloom mountains, Co. Offaly.
12. Goll Mac Morna.
13. She was the daughter of Cormac Mac Art.
14. Manannan Mac Lir.
15. 'Glaine ar gcroi 'gus neart ar ngeag is beart de reir ar mbriathair' ('Truth in our hearts, strength in our arms, and faith in our tongues').

Custom and Tradition (*page 57*)

1. Yew.
2. Lands allocated by a clan for the support of its clergy.
3. Holly.
4. Hazel.
5. The Irish tonsure took the form of shaving the hair at the front of the head, allowing the back to grow long; Roman tonsure shaved the crown of the head.
6. First — missionaries; second — monks, teachers and clerics; third — hermits.
7. Seven.

8. During times of pestilence, famine or drought.
9. The relationship between the parents of a child and the child's godfather.
10. Homicide or personal injury.
11. Anyone who contravened the peace was put to death.
12. The heir-apparent.
13. *Book of Acaill.*
14. *Scriptorium.*
15. Twelve.

1916 (*page 58*)

1. Augustine Birrell.
2. Michael Mallin.
3. Bishop O'Dwyer of Limerick.
4. Captain J. C. Bowen-Colthurst (subsequently found guilty of murder but adjudged insane).
5. Sir Matthew Nathan.
6. Commdt Eamon de Valera.
7. Commdt Thomas MacDonagh.
8. At Bawnard House, Fermoy, Co. Cork, home of the Kent family, on Saturday, 29 April.
9. Sixty-four.
10. Patrick Pearse, Thomas J. Clarke and Thomas Mac Donagh.
11. 'In order to prevent the further slaughter of Dublin citizens, and in the hope of saving the lives of our followers now surrounded . . .'.
12. Rory O'Connor.
13. Michael Collins.
14. *Irish War News.*

Northern Politics (*page 59*)

1. H. M. Pollock.
2. Minister for Finance.
3. H. V. Kirk.

4. Brian Faulkner.
5. Forty (1921).
6. Eleven (1929).
7. Eight.
8. Nineteen.
9. Faulknerite Unionists (twenty-four).
10. One.
11. Labour.
12. E. M. Archdale.
13. Third Duke of Abercorn (December 1922–September 1945).
14. Gerry Fitt (now Lord Fitt of Bell's Hill).
15. David Bleakley (1971).

Politics from 1950 (*page 60*)

1. Department of Transport and Power.
2. William Norton.
3. Donough O'Malley.
4. Sean MacEntee.
5. Frank Aiken.
6. Erskine Childers.
7. Patrick Donegan.
8. Neil T. Blaney.
9. Brian Lenihan.
10. Minister for Health.
11. Robert Molloy.
12. George Colley.
13. Department of the Public Service (1 November 1973).
14. Anthony J. Hederman.
15. Colm Condon.

Around Munster (*page 61*)

1. Mrs Blennerhassett.
2. Sean Keating (1889–1977).
3. Cloyne.

4. St Finbarr's South.
5. In the Fr Mathew Memorial Church, Fr Mathew Quay (a stained-glass window).
6. Richard Bagwell (1840–1918).
7. Joseph Halliday (b. 1775).
8. King John, in 1205.
9. Isaac Butt.
10. Eugene O'Curry (1796–1862).
11. The Burren.
12. Kenmare, Co. Kerry.
13. Robin Flower (*The Islandman*, 1934).
14. Corofin.

The Irish Theatre (*page 62*)

1. *St Patrick for Ireland* at Dublin's Werburgh Street, 1643.
2. John Ogilby (Ogilvy).
3. Peg Woffington (c. 1714–60).
4. Spranger Barry (1719–77).
5. Charles McLoughlin (c. 1697–1797).
6. Dion Boucicault (1820–90).
7. Sean O'Casey (1880–1964).
8. Duras House, Kinvara, Co. Galway.
9. Persse.
10. She was prompted by a reading of the Tarot cards and astrological charts.
11. Because the Theatre remained open on the day of King Edward's death.
12. Philadelphia.

Mo Sceal Fein (My Own Story) (*page 63*)

1. That of An tAthair Peadar O' Laoghaire (1839–1920).
2. Maud Gonne MacBride's (1865–1953).
3. Those of Thomas J. Clarke (1857–1916).
4. Sir Charles Gavan Duffy (1816–1903).
5. Augusta, Lady Gregory (1852–1932).

6. *Down All the Days*.
7. Robert Brennan (1881–1964).
8. Dan Breen (1894–1969).
9. Austin Clarke (1896–1974).
10. *Stone Mad*.
11. Peig Sayers' (1873–1958).
12. Those of Frank Gallagher ('David Hogan') (1898–1962).
13. Frank O' Connor's (1903–66).
14. W. B. Yeats (1865–1939).

Works of History (*page 64*)

1. John O'Donovan (1809–61).
2. Eoin MacNeill (1867–1945).
3. Sean O'Riordain (1905–57).
4. Margaret Stokes.
5. R. R. Madden (1798–1886).
6. Robin Flower (1881–1946).
7. Myles Dillon (1900–1972).
8. Whitley Stokes (1830–1909).
9. Maire and Liam de Paor.
10. Edward MacLysaght (1887–1986).
11. A. M. Sullivan (1830–84).
12. Henry Boylan.
13. Richard Irvine Best (1872–1959).
14. James Anthony Froude (1818–94).
15. Constantia Maxwell (1886–1962).

Young Ireland (*page 65*)

1. John Mitchel (1815–75).
2. John O'Connell (1810–58).
3. Treason-Felony Act.
4. Fr John Kenyon (1812–69).
5. William Smith O'Brien (1803–64).
6. Isaac Butt (1813–79).
7. Pope Pius IX.

8. Dr Robert Cane (1807–58).
9. Terence Bellew MacManus (1811–61).
10. Inspector Trant.
11. Thomas Devin Reilly (1824–54).
12. Chartists.
13. Thomas D'Arcy Magee.
14. Celebrating revolution in France.

The Great Hunger (*page 66*)

1. Sir Robert Peel.
2. Lord Heytesbury.
3. Lord Bessborough.
4. Dr Lyon Playfair and Dr John Lindley.
5. £100,000.
6. Ballinglass.
7. Thomas Campbell Foster.
8. Sir Charles Wood.
9. Lord John Russell.
10. £2,000.
11. Major-General Sir John Burgoyne.
12. Cobh (which was then re-named Queenstown).
13. James Fintan Lalor.
14. Timothy O'Brien.
15. T. N. Redington.

People and Places (*page 67*)

1. William Roche, MP ('Roche's Folly').
2. John Roberts.
3. Albert Power.
4. Ten per cent of all wine imported into Ireland.
5. Dundalk (the Kelly Monument).
6. Clonmel, Co. Tipperary (a building).
7. Thomas Kirk (1781–1845) who also designed the Tramore 'Metal Man'.
8. Five.

9. Tralee (Courthouse).
10. Longford O'Farrell.
11. Monaghan .
12. Roscommon.
13. Trim, Co. Meath.

The Last Set (*page 68*)

1. Smock Alley.
2. Donnybrook Fair, Dublin.
3. Lord FitzAlan.
4. Domhnall Ua Buachalla (Daniel Buckley).
5. Gortroe, Rathcormac, Co. Cork.
6. John Nash.
7. Sean Lester.
8. Robert Barton (d. 10 August 1975).
9. Sir Hamar Greenwood.
10. It was the last in these islands to be horse-drawn.
11. Rory O'Connor (d. 1198).
12. Eamon de Valera.
13. Joseph Plunkett.
14. Roger Casement.
15. William Mulready (1786–1863).